THE SOMATIC THERAPY HANDBOOK

A TRANSFORMATIVE GUIDE TO TRAUMA
RECOVERY, ANXIETY RELIEF, NERVOUS SYSTEM
REGULATION AND RELEASING EMOTIONAL
BLOCKAGES BY CONNECTING MIND,
BODY & SOUL

Y.D. GARDENS

THE EMERALD
SOCIETY

A SPECIAL GIFT TO MY READERS

Visit emeraldsocpublishing.com to download your FREE copy!

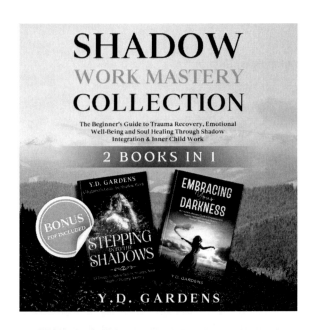

Now Available on Amazon, Audible & iTunes!

LEAVE A REVIEW

Don't forget to share the love and **leave your Amazon review** for:

The Somatic Therapy Handbook

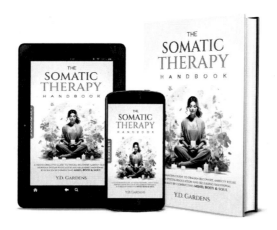

PREFACE

Dear Soul-Searcher,

IN THE VAST expanse of human emotion and experience, it is the quiet moments of connection between mind, body, and soul that often go unnoticed. Yet, these often imperceptible time lapses hold the key to our most profound healing and understanding.

After a few years of taking a deep dive into shadow work, I felt compelled to create this complete somatics toolkit. This is my way of extending a heartfelt invitation to women like yourself to embark on the most significant journey you will ever undertake—the journey inward. Somatic healing has come to be not only an important addition to my work exploring inner child wounds and shadow webs; it is now clearly an inevitable component of this holistic healing journey.

You see, my own path to discovering the power of somatic

therapy began in a place of darkness, a period when the weight of unspoken trauma seemed to cloud every aspect of my existence. It was a time when anxiety was a constant companion, whispering doubts and fears into my ear, chaining me to memories and sensations I felt powerless to escape. The turning point came unexpectedly, through the gentle guidance of a wonderful therapist and several holistic healers, who taught me the transformative power of tuning into my body's wisdom. Little by little, I learned to listen to the subtle cues my body was giving me—tension, breath, heartbeat—and to respond with compassion rather than fear.

The true turning point, however, was learning to connect these physiological sensations to my thoughts, thus to my perceptions and reactions.

One particularly profound moment stands out. During a therapy session a few years ago, I was asked to close my eyes and, as I pictured a triggering past event in my mind, I was told to notice the sensations in my body, without judgment. It was uncomfortable at first, to say the least. But as I continued to focus and breathe into spaces of tension, I instinctively released a tightly held breath I didn't even know I was holding. In that moment, a surge of emotion overwhelmed me, and tears began flowing freely not from pain, but from a deep sense of release. It was as if my body was finally allowed to speak its truth, and in doing so, began the process of letting go of years of stored trauma. This experience was a game changer, illuminating the next steps of my path toward healing and wholeness.

Drawing from these deeply personal encounters with somatic healing, this all in one guide-journal-workbook is designed to be a compassionate companion on your journey. Each page is crafted with the intention of guiding you gently toward discovering your own body's wisdom, providing tools to release stored trauma, and offering practices to cultivate a harmonious connection between your mind, body, and soul.

As you engage with the information, exercises and reflections within these pages, remember that the journey of healing is not linear. There will be moments of challenge and resistance, but also moments of profound insight and liberation. Also, you should know that this is not a race to the finish line - in fact, there is no ending. I therefore encourage you to respect the ebb and flow of your own life story, and to be gentle with yourself as you go through this work. This workbook is here to support you through it all, offering a safe space to explore, heal, and grow.

I hope this guide serves as hope and a testament to the resilience of the human spirit. My deepest wish is that through these practices, you too will experience the transformative power of connecting with your body's innate wisdom.

Here's to your journey of healing, discovery, and ultimately, tapping into that delicious space of inner peace.

WELCOME to the beginning of a new chapter.

INTRODUCTION

Have you ever stood at the edge of the ocean, toes buried in the sand, watching the waves wash away your footprints with effortless ease? There is a profound lesson in this simple act of nature: just as the water smooths the sands of time, somatic therapy holds the power to gently cleanse our being, releasing us from the grip of past traumas and anxiety. You should know that the journey toward healing and self-discovery can be as transformative as the ocean's relentless reshaping of the shoreline. This book is your invitation to explore the depths of somatic therapy, a practice that has not only changed lives but has also provided a healing path for many - myself included.

My dedication to the realm of women's mental health and wellness is not just a professional choice; it is a calling that has shaped my life's work. Through years of experience and a deeply rooted passion for guiding women through their emotional barricades, I have come to understand the intricate dance of mind, body, and soul. My belief in the transformative power of integrating these aspects of our being is what led me to somatic therapy—a path that promises harmonious balance that beckons inner peace.

This book was crafted with you in mind. Whether you are new to the concept of somatic therapy or looking to deepen your practice, this guide is designed to be your best companion. Picking up this book is already a testament to the strength within you, ready to be discovered and nurtured. Here, you will find a blend of information, advice, practical tools, and heartfelt wisdom, all aimed at guiding you towards holistic healing.

As you have probably already noticed, the tone of this book is much like a supportive friend—compassionate, encouraging, and filled with hope. My aim was to create a space where jargon does not hinder understanding, and the complex becomes accessible, no matter your experience. You will soon discover that this unique approach combines informational content with practical workbook activities and journaling prompts, encouraging you to not just read or listen, but engage, reflect, and grow. This was designed to ensure a comprehensive understanding of somatic therapy principles, whilst empowering you to actively engage and apply these learnings immediately in your daily life.

Perhaps you've already begun your journey of inner work and know that it is as profound as it is personal. I firmly believe that the release from anxiety, recovery from trauma, and a deepened connection between your mind, body, and soul is the greatest gift you can offer yourself. This promise of finding inner peace and achieving a state of harmonious balance that once may have seemed out of reach is absolutely life-changing.

So, I now invite you to dive in with an open heart and mind, ready to explore the depths of your being. Take as much time as is needed to digest the informational content. Engage fully with the exercises and reflections provided, for the path to healing and inner peace begins with this very step. Let us navigate these waters together, with the promise that on the other side, a renewed sense of self awaits.

Somatics:

A field within bodywork and movement studies which emphasizes internal physical perception and experience.

ONE

SOMATICS: THE ORIGINS

I n the midst of a world brimming with rapid advancements and technological marvels, we often find our essence tethered to the past, weighed down by experiences that shape our present yet remain untouched and unexplored. It's within this complexity of human experience that somatic therapy emerges, not as a mere method of healing but as a profound dialogue between body and soul. This chapter unfolds the mosaic of somatic therapy, tracing its lineage from ancient wisdom to contemporary practice, and shedding light on its transformative power.

The Origins of Somatic Therapy: A Historical Overview

The roots of somatic therapy stretch deep into the soil of human history, intertwined with the earliest practices of healing and spirituality. Long before the advent of modern medicine, ancient civilizations understood the inseparable connection between the body and the mind. In the healing temples of Egypt, the therapeutic baths of Rome, and the yogic traditions of India, we find the precursors to somatic therapy. These cultures recognized that physical ailments often have emotional and spiritual components, a concept that forms the cornerstone of somatic therapy today.

Wilhelm Reich, a student of Freud, laid the groundwork for what would become somatic therapy in the early 20th century. Reich proposed that psychological trauma manifests physically as "body armors", constricting the flow of vital energy. His revolutionary ideas paved the way for further exploration into the mind-body connection. Peter Levine, another pivotal figure, expanded on this foundation with his development of Somatic Experiencing® in the latter part of the century. Drawing from observations of how animals process stress and trauma, Levine's work offered a new perspective on human trauma recovery, emphasizing the body's inherent ability to heal itself.

The influence of diverse cultures on somatic practices cannot be understated. From the mindfulness of Buddhist meditation to the rhythmic movements of African dance, global traditions have enriched the fabric of somatic therapy, introducing a variety of techniques that cater to the multifaceted nature of human healing. This integration of perspectives underscores the universal truth that healing transcends cultural boundaries, resonating with the core of our shared humanity.

As somatic therapy gained traction, its applications broadened, touching the lives of people seeking relief from the vestiges of trauma, stress, and disconnection. Today, somatic therapy enjoys a revered place in healing and wellness communities, highlighting its effectiveness and holistic approach. Far from a one-size-fits-all solution, it offers a personalized path to wellness, acknowledging the unique stories etched in our bodies and spirits.

In a coffee shop, a place seemingly distant from the quiet introspection of therapy, one might observe a microcosm of somatic principles at play. Notice how a deep breath and a moment of mindfulness can cut through the noise of a busy day, grounding us in the present. This simple act, a practice deeply rooted in somatic therapy, illustrates the profound impact of reconnecting with our bodily sensations, offering a momentary respite from the whirlwind of thoughts and emotions. It's in these everyday moments that the essence of somatics comes to life, bridging the ancient and the modern in the quest for healing and balance.

The journey of somatics, from its ancient origins to its current prominence, reflects a growing recognition of the body's wisdom and the healing power of mindful presence. As we continue to explore and expand upon these practices, we'll draw closer to a more integrated and holistic understanding of health and well-being, one that honors the intricate dance between body, mind, and spirit.

Mind, Body, Spirit: The Triad of Holistic Healing

Within somatic therapy, the threads of mind, body, and spirit weave together, supporting holistic healing that is both intricate and profound. This fusion is foundational, asserting that these elements are not separate entities but deeply interconnected aspects of our being. This recognition shifts the focus from treating isolated symptoms to nurturing the whole person, a perspective that is both revolutionary and as ancient as humanity itself.

Interconnectedness

The principle of interconnectedness lies at the heart of

somatic therapy. It posits that the mind influences the body just as the body influences the mind, with the spirit acting as the bridge between the two. This triad forms a complex system where changes in one aspect invariably affect the others. For instance, a prolonged state of stress can lead not only to mental health issues like anxiety but also to physical symptoms such as tension headaches or digestive problems, reflecting the body's distress. Similarly, a chronic physical condition can lead to depression or anxiety, demonstrating the body's impact on the mind. The spirit, in this context, encompasses our sense of self, purpose, and connection to something greater than ourselves, influencing and being influenced by the state of our mind and body.

Holistic Health

The concept of holistic health emerges naturally from the interconnectedness of mind, body, and spirit. It advocates for a comprehensive approach to well-being that considers all aspects of the individual. In practice, this means addressing more than physical symptoms by also exploring emotional, psychological, and spiritual dimensions. This approach promotes deep, lasting healing and transformation, as it acknowledges and addresses the root causes of imbalance rather than merely alleviating symptoms. For those navigating the challenges of stress and trauma, this holistic approach offers a path to recovery that is both thorough and empathetic, recognizing the individual as a complex, multifaceted being.

The Impact of Stress and Trauma

Stress and trauma, often seen as primarily psychological

issues, reverberate through the mind, body, and spirit, highlighting the necessity of a holistic healing approach. The physical manifestations of stress and trauma can range from tense muscles and headaches to more severe conditions like fibromyalgia or chronic fatigue syndrome. Psychologically, they can lead to anxiety, depression, and PTSD, affecting one's sense of self and place in the world. Spiritually, trauma can leave individuals feeling disconnected, lost, or without purpose. Somatic therapy, with its holistic lens, recognizes these intricate connections and addresses the multifaceted impact of stress and trauma, facilitating healing on all levels.

The Path to Wellness

Somatic therapy charts a course towards wellness that honors and nurtures the connection between mind, body, and spirit. It employs a variety of techniques, from mindful body scanning and breathing exercises to movement and expressive arts, each designed to foster awareness, release stored trauma, and promote integration and healing. This path is not linear but is tailored to the individual's unique experiences, needs, and pacing.

Consider, for example, the practice of mindful body scanning. This technique encourages us to tune into our body, noticing sensations without judgment. This simple act creates a deeper connection with our physical self, revealing areas of tension or numbness that may be holding emotional pain. By bringing awareness to these areas and gently exploring their emotional context, we can begin to release and heal trauma wounds stored within our body.

Breathing exercises offer another powerful tool for reconnecting the mind, body, and spirit. Controlled breathing not only calms the mind and reduces stress but also helps to regulate the body's physiological response to stress. On a spiritual level, breathwork can be a meditative practice that promotes inner peace and connectedness.

Movement practices, whether through yoga, dance, or simple stretching, allow individuals to express and release emotions physically, facilitating psychological healing. These also strengthen the body-mind connection, enhancing physical health and a general feeling of wholeness.

For those navigating the aftermath of trauma, techniques like Somatic Experiencing® offer a structured approach to processing and integrating traumatic experiences. By focusing on bodily sensations and employing titration to gradually work through trauma, this method allows for safe, controlled healing, addressing the impact of trauma on the mind, body, and spirit.

The path to wellness offered by somatic therapy is a journey of self-discovery, healing, and transformation. It recognizes the individual as a whole, honoring the complex interplay between mind, body, and spirit. Through a combination of awareness, expression, and integration, somatic therapy provides a path to a more balanced, peaceful, and fulfilling life.

Principles of Somatic Therapy: Core Beliefs and Practices

Somatic therapy operates on foundational principles that distinguish it from other therapeutic modalities. These principles guide the practice, ensuring that healing is not only effective but also holistic and empowering.

Body as the Primary Focus

Central to somatic therapy is the recognition of the body as both the repository of trauma and the vehicle for healing. This view challenges conventional approaches that prioritize the mind in understanding and treating psychological distress. Instead, somatic therapy posits that the body holds onto traumatic experiences, manifesting them through various physical symptoms and patterns. By focusing on the body, somatic therapy engages directly with the source of trauma, offering a pathway to release and heal these deep-seated wounds.

This principle is evident in the way somatic therapy approaches the treatment of anxiety, for instance. Traditional therapy might explore the thoughts and beliefs contributing to anxiety, offering cognitive strategies to manage it. Somatic therapy, while not dismissing the value of understanding the mind's role, dives deeper into the bodily sensations associated with anxiety. It explores how anxiety is experienced in the body—the tightness in the chest, the quickening of the breath, the tension in the shoulders—and uses this awareness as a starting point for healing.

The Wisdom of the Body

Somatic therapy teaches that the body possesses an intrinsic wisdom, capable of guiding us towards understanding and healing. This wisdom speaks through the language of sensations, impulses, and movements, communicating needs, boundaries, and unresolved emotions. Learning to listen and interpret these signals is a fundamental aspect of somatic therapy. It requires cultivating a deep sense of body awareness, a process that can be both challenging and liberating.

For example, consider the experience of feeling a knot in the stomach when faced with a difficult decision. This physical sensation is the body's way of signaling stress or fear, perhaps pointing to underlying concerns or doubts. Somatic therapy encourages us to explore these sensations with curiosity, allowing them to unfold and reveal the emotions and memories they contain. This is a process which helps develop self-awareness whilst supporting emotional processing and resolution.

Integration of Experiences

Similar to aspects of shadow work, the key aim of somatic therapy is the integration of traumatic experiences, facilitating a process of healing that is both comprehensive and sustainable. As we know, integration involves acknowledging and processing traumatic memories, rather than simply reliving them - a distinction that is crucial to understand. Integrating traumatic experiences involves a gentle and controlled exploration of the trauma, guided by the body's wisdom and, if possible, a therapist's support.

Integration sees traumatic experiences as fragmented pieces of the self that have been disowned or disconnected due to their overwhelming nature. Through somatic therapy, these pieces are gradually acknowledged, felt, and understood within the safety of the therapeutic relationship. This process allows for a reconnection with these disowned parts, leading to a sense of wholeness and coherence. The integration of traumatic experiences transforms how these memories are held within the body and the mind, moving from sources of distress to aspects of the self that have been healed and reclaimed.

Empowerment through Self-Regulation

At its core, somatic therapy is about empowerment. It will equip you with skills for self-regulation, enhancing your ability to manage your emotional and physiological states. Self-regulation is vital in navigating the stresses and challenges of life, promoting resilience and a sense of agency. As you'll soon discover, somatic therapy offers practical tools and exercises that strengthen the capacity for self-regulation, such as meditative practices, grounding techniques, and intuitive movement.

Mindful breathing, for instance, is a simple yet powerful tool for self-regulation. By focusing on the breath and consciously slowing it down, individuals can directly influence their nervous system, shifting from a state of alertness and stress to one of calm and relaxation. This ability to regulate one's state is empowering, offering a way to manage anxiety, stress, and emotional overwhelm independently.

Grounding techniques serve a similar purpose, helping us anchor in the present moment when faced with distressing emotions or memories. These techniques, which often involve engaging the senses or focusing on physical sensations, provide a means to stabilize and center ourselves. Whether it's feeling the texture of a fabric, focusing on the sensation of feet touching the ground, or listening to the sounds in our environment, grounding techniques help make us feel safe and in control.

Also, movement practices, from yoga and dance to simple stretching exercises, play a key role in self-regulation. They allow for the expression and release of pent-up emotions, facilitating emotional equilibrium. Movement connects the mind and body, promoting an integrated experience of self-awareness and emotional processing.

The empowerment that comes from mastering self-regulation skills is transformative. It shifts the narrative from one of victimhood or helplessness to one of strength and agency. We can learn to trust in our ability to navigate our internal world, managing emotional and physiological states with confidence and skill. This empowerment shows the capacity for resilience and healing inherent in each person, one that somatic therapy seeks to awaken and nurture.

The Science of Somatics: How It Works in the Brain and Body

The dance between our physical experiences and psychological states finds a compelling explanation within the realm of neurobiology, particularly when examining the impact of trauma. Trauma, often perceived through a purely psychological lens, leaves indelible marks on both the brain and nervous system, illustrating the profound interconnectedness of our mental and physical wellbeing.

If you're ready, we will briefly dive into some of the scientific underpinnings of somatic therapy. The purpose here is to shed light on its effectiveness in healing trauma by bridging the gap between body and mind, so that we can better understand the 'what' and 'how' before jumping into practice.

Neurobiology of Trauma

Recent advancements in neuroscience have provided invaluable insights into how traumatic events alter the brain's structure and function. Trauma can dysregulate the brain's fear circuitry, particularly the amygdala, hippocampus, and prefrontal cortex, leading to heightened states of anxiety and an impaired ability to process emotions. The amygdala, responsible for detecting threats, becomes overly reactive, while the hippocampus, crucial for memory consolidation, may shrink, impacting an individual's ability to contextualize fear. Conversely, the prefrontal cortex, which governs reasoning and impulse control, may show reduced activity, making it challenging to regulate emotions and responses to perceived threats. This dysregulation contributes to the persistent feeling of being "stuck" that many trauma survivors experience, unable to move past the traumatic event.

The Role of the Nervous System

Central to somatic therapy is an understanding of the autonomic nervous system (ANS), which regulates involuntary bodily functions, including heartbeat, digestion, and respiratory rate. The ANS comprises two main branches: the sympathetic nervous system (SNS), which triggers the "fight or flight" response during perceived threats, and the parasympathetic nervous system (PNS), which promotes "rest and digest" functions, restoring calm and balance after the threat has passed. Trauma can lead to an imbalance, with the SNS remaining in a hyperactivated state, leaving us in a constant state of alertness and tension.

Here's what you need to remember: Somatic therapy aims to restore balance within the autonomic nervous system. To do this, we employ techniques that activate the parasympathetic nervous system to counteract this hyperarousal (stress) and facilitate a state of relaxation and safety.

Body-Brain Feedback Loop

The relationship between the body and the brain is not unidirectional but rather a continuous feedback loop, where bodily sensations affect mental states and vice versa. This loop is crucial in understanding somatic therapy. For instance, the act of taking slow, deep breaths—a common somatic practice— can signal the brain to lower stress levels, demonstrating how physical actions can influence psychological wellbeing. Similarly, adopting a posture of confidence can not only reflect but also generate feelings of self-assuredness. Somatic therapy leverages this feedback loop, using physical sensations and movements to influence emotional and mental states, creating an environment where healing can occur from the inside out.

Evidence-Based Practices

The effectiveness of somatic therapy in treating trauma is supported by a growing body of research. Studies have shown that somatic practices, such as mindful movement and breathwork, can significantly reduce symptoms of PTSD, anxiety, and depression. These practices help reduce symptoms of hyperarousal and increase feelings of safety and grounding. Furthermore, neuroimaging research has revealed that somatic therapy can lead to changes in brain areas impacted by trauma, such as increased hippocampal volume and reduced amygdala reactivity, pointing to its potential in facilitating not only psychological but also neurological healing.

One compelling study observed the effects of Somatic Experiencing on individuals with PTSD. Participants reported significant reductions in PTSD symptoms, including flashbacks, anxiety, and sleep disturbances. These findings were mirrored in physiological measures, with participants showing decreased heart rate and increased heart rate variability, indicators of a more balanced ANS. These results demonstrate the potential of somatic therapy to address the root causes of trauma, offering a holistic approach to healing that encompasses both mind and body.

As you are now well aware, understanding the science of somatics allows us to demystify the mechanisms through which somatic therapy facilitates healing from trauma. By addressing the neurobiological and physiological impacts of trauma, somatic therapy offers a comprehensive approach that honors the intricate connection between the brain and the body. As you continue to move through these chapters, you'll discover targeted practices that engage this connection and will lead you on a path of healing, moving beyond the shadows of your past and towards a future marked by balance, resilience, and well-being.

Somatic Therapy vs. Traditional Therapy

In the area of therapeutic practices, the distinction between somatic therapy and traditional therapeutic modalities is as profound as it is pivotal. This differentiation is not only academic but touches the very essence of how healing is approached, experienced, and integrated by those who seek relief from the shadows cast by trauma.

Approach to Trauma

At the heart of somatic therapy lies an emphasis on bodily sensations and experiences as the gateway to understanding and healing trauma. This contrasts with the cognitive or talk therapy focus, which predominantly navigates thoughts, beliefs, and narratives. While traditional therapy often seeks to untangle the cognitive webs surrounding traumatic experiences, somatic therapy plunges directly into the body's memory of the event, exploring the non-verbal cues and sensations that are frequently bypassed in verbal recounting. This approach acknowledges that trauma often resides deeper than words can reach, manifesting in physical symptoms like tension, breathlessness, or numbness. By tuning into these bodily signals, somatic therapy facilitates a direct engagement with the trauma, offering a pathway to release and healing that circumvents the sometimes-limiting framework of language.

The Role of the Therapist

The role of the therapist in somatic therapy diverges significantly from traditional approaches, embodying a facilitative rather than directive presence. Somatic therapists act as guides, helping individuals to cultivate awareness of their bodily sensations and to interpret these signals as meaningful narratives about their experiences and traumas. This contrasts with the more directive role often assumed by traditional therapists, who may steer conversations, interpret psychological patterns, or suggest cognitive strategies for coping with distress.

In somatic therapy, the therapist and client embark on a collaborative journey, with the therapist supporting the client's exploration of their internal landscape. This partnership is predicated on trust, with the therapist providing a safe and non-judgmental space for the client to reconnect with their body's wisdom and capacity for self-healing.

Treatment Outcomes

Considering treatment outcomes, somatic therapy offers distinctive benefits, particularly in addressing deep-seated trauma. Traditional therapy has been instrumental in providing insights into the psychological dimensions of trauma, offering strategies for managing symptoms and reshaping cognitive narratives. However, for some, this may not fully address the somatic imprint of trauma, which can linger in the body's memory, manifesting as chronic pain, tension, or dysregulated arousal states.

Somatic therapy, by focusing on the body's role in trauma and healing, provides a complementary pathway to wellness. It allows for the release of stored trauma and the reintegration of the self, leading to outcomes that encompass mental and emotional healing, as well as physical relief and a renewed sense of embodiment. Somatic practitioners often report a greater sense of connection to their bodies, improved emotional regulation, and a decrease in physiological symptoms associated with trauma.

Accessibility and Inclusivity

One of the most compelling aspects of somatic therapy is its accessibility and inclusivity. Traditional therapy, with its reliance on verbal communication, can inadvertently exclude those who may find it difficult to articulate their experiences or emotions, such as individuals with certain disabilities, young children, or those for whom language is a barrier. Somatic therapy, with its non-verbal approach, opens the door to healing for a broader spectrum of individuals. It transcends linguistic and cognitive limitations, making it particularly valuable for diverse populations. This inclusivity extends to cultural considerations as well. The somatic healing focus on universal bodily experiences allows it to bridge cultural gaps, providing a form of healing that resonates on a fundamentally human level, irrespective of an individual's background or language.

In sum, the landscape of therapeutic practices is rich and varied, with each approach offering its unique pathways to healing. With its focus on the body's wisdom and capacity for healing, somatic therapy offers a distinctive and valuable complement to traditional therapeutic modalities. By engaging directly with the body's memory of trauma and facilitating a deep, non-verbal process of healing, somatic therapy expands the possibilities for recovery and wellness. It emphasizes a collaborative and facilitative approach, empowering us to become active participants in our healing journey. Furthermore, its accessibility and inclusivity make it a vital resource for individuals across a broad spectrum of experiences and backgrounds, underscoring its importance in the field of mental health and wellness.

MIND & BODY

> *The body is our gauge of truth, our inner oracle - and when we're disconnected from it, we're disconnected from our innate intuitive strengths and our primal gut instincts.*

ALETHEIA LUNA

TWO
THE BODY'S TALE

Your body is like a vast library - each cell a book, each muscle a tome of memories. Within this library, stories of joy and sorrow, pleasure and pain are archived, not always consciously accessed but ever-present.

I'm offering this perspective for you to consider how deeply your experiences, particularly traumatic ones, are embedded within your physical self. It's not just about scars seen by the eye but about those felt only when you tune into the silent whispers of your body.

In this exploration, we turn our focus to understanding trauma's impact on the body. The aim is to shed light on the often-overlooked somatic symptoms of trauma, guiding us through recognizing these signs and gently releasing the stories they hold. This understanding acknowledges the presence of trauma and empowers us with knowledge and techniques to navigate through its somatic expressions towards healing.

Trauma has a profound impact on the body, often triggering a chronic stress response. This is not merely a psychological state but a physiological one, where the body is perpetually in a "fight or flight" mode. Such constant vigilance can manifest as tension in the muscles, a rapid heartbeat, or even disrupted digestive and immune systems. Over time, these responses, meant to protect us in moments of danger, can become our default state, leading to a range of physical health issues from chronic pain to autoimmune diseases.

Somatization

Somatization is a phenomenon where emotional distress is expressed through physical pain. When trauma is not processed or expressed emotionally, the body becomes a vessel for this unspoken pain, manifesting symptoms without a clear medical cause. For instance, someone might experience severe stomach aches during periods of stress or headaches when recalling a traumatic event. These are not just random occurrences and should not be reduced to regular bodily functions: They are the body's way of signaling unresolved emotional turmoil.

The Concept of 'Body Memory'

The idea that our bodies remember traumatic events, even when our minds may not fully recall them, is central to understanding somatization and the physiological effects of trauma. This 'body memory' can surface through sudden, unexplained physical reactions to certain people, places, or situations that are reminiscent of the trauma. It's as if the body has its own alarm system, alerting us to potential danger based on past experiences. Recognizing these reactions as memories rather than immediate threats is a crucial step in the healing process.

Releasing Trauma

Facilitating the release of trauma stored in the body is a delicate process, requiring patience, compassion, and often guided support. Techniques vary, but the goal is the same: to allow the body to express and let go of the trauma it holds. This can be achieved through:

- Mindful Movement: Practices like yoga or tai chi encourage attentiveness to bodily sensations, creating a space for the body to communicate its stored traumas and begin the process of releasing them.
- Breath Work: Controlled breathing exercises can help regulate the body's stress response, creating a sense of safety that allows for the release of tension and trauma.
- Body Scanning: By mentally scanning the body and noticing areas of tension or discomfort, individuals can begin to identify where trauma might be stored and approach these areas with gentle awareness and curiosity.

As we continue, we will explore these further and learn how incorporating these techniques into daily routines can significantly impact how trauma is held and processed in the body. For example, starting the day with a few moments of deep, mindful breathing can set a tone of calm and presence. Similarly, integrating gentle stretches or yoga poses into breaks throughout the day can help release physical tension and remind us to stay connected with our bodies.

Our bodies communicate with us constantly, sending signals about our physical and emotional well-being through a language of sensations, pulses, and movements. This form of communication is subtle, often overlooked in the noise of daily life, yet it holds insights into our inner world. This section aims to illuminate the process of tuning into the body's language, interpreting its messages, and responding with care and compassion.

Developing Body Awareness

Increasing awareness of bodily sensations is akin to tuning an instrument, refining our ability to detect the subtle nuances of our internal experience. Here are several strategies designed to heighten this awareness:

- Scheduled Check-ins: Set aside specific times each day to pause and scan your body. Notice any areas of tension, discomfort, or ease without trying to change anything. This practice helps in cultivating a habit of listening to your body.
- Mindfulness Meditation: Engage in mindfulness meditation, focusing your attention on different parts of your body. Observe the sensations without judgment, allowing yourself to become more attuned to your body's language.
- Movement Exploration: I have a soft spot for this one, as it is certainly one of my favorite ways to reconnect with my breath and body. I recommend experimenting with different forms of movement, such as stretching, dancing, or walking. Pay

attention to how each movement feels and what it reveals about your body's state.

Interpreting Signals

Our body's signals are messages about our needs, boundaries, and unresolved issues. Learning to interpret these signals involves a deep attunement to our physical sensations and the emotions they evoke. Here are three ways in which to decipher the body's communications.

1. Connecting Sensations to Emotions: When you notice a physical sensation, such as a tight chest or clenched jaw, ask yourself what emotion might be linked to this sensation. Is it anxiety, anger, or perhaps something else?

2. Historical Context: Reflect on whether the sensation is familiar or linked to a specific event or period in your life. Understanding the historical context can provide clues about unresolved issues or traumas. This is also very useful for inner child healing.

3. Somatic Journaling: Keep a journal of bodily sensations and their possible meanings. Over time, patterns may emerge that offer deeper insights into your emotional world.

Case Studies

To illustrate the transformative power of listening to and responding to your body's language, I've decided to share four short stories. Although I've left out some details about each person's journey, I'm hoping that these may shed some light on how somatics can support you on your own path to reconnecting with yourself.

Case 1: Anna's Journey of Reconnection

After years of chronic tension headaches, Anna began practicing daily body check-ins, discovering a link between her headaches and unexpressed anger. Through somatic therapy and mindfulness practices, she learned to acknowledge and express her emotions in healthy ways, leading to a significant reduction in her headaches.

Case 2: Mark's Path to Emotional Freedom

Mark experienced sudden panic attacks with no apparent trigger. Through somatic experiencing® therapy, he uncovered that certain physical sensations were triggering memories of a car accident he had been in years before. By working through these body memories in a safe and supportive environment, Mark was able to process the trauma, leading to a cessation of his panic attacks.

Case 3: Lily's Discovery of Boundaries

Lily often found herself feeling drained after social interactions. Through mindful movement and body scanning, she realized that her energy levels dropped significantly in certain company. This awareness helped her set healthier boundaries in her relationships, improving her energy and emotional well-being.

These three case studies, although briefly summarized, show aspects of the healing that becomes possible when we attune to our body's language, interpret its messages, and respond with compassion and intention.

Checklist of Somatic Symptoms

Trauma can manifest physically in various ways, often without a direct or immediate connection to the traumatic event itself. This is a comprehensive checklist of somatic symptoms that can be useful in identifying potential signs of unprocessed trauma.

Physical Sensations and Pain

- Chronic pain in muscles and joints
- Stomach pain and digestive issues
- Sudden, unexplained headaches
- Pervasive fatigue or exhaustion
- Extreme sensitivity to cold and heat

Cardiovascular and Respiratory Symptoms

- Rapid heartbeat or palpitations
- Difficulty breathing or shortness of breath
- Feelings of pressure or tightness in the chest

Immune System and Health Changes

- Frequent illnesses or infections
- Changes in appetite, significant weight loss or gain
- Sleep disturbances, insomnia, or oversleeping

Neurological and Sensory Symptoms

- Hyperarousal or hypervigilance
- Numbness or tingling in different parts of the body
- Heightened sensitivity to light, sound, or touch

Motor Functions

- Tremors or uncontrollable shaking
- Difficulty coordinating movements or clumsiness
- Startle response more pronounced or easily triggered

Other Physical Symptoms

- Dizziness or feeling faint
- Skin issues (e.g., rashes, eczema triggered by stress)
- Sexual dysfunction or loss of libido

Emotional Responses Connected to Physical Symptoms

- Physical symptoms that worsen with stress or emotional distress
- Somatic symptoms that flare up around anniversaries of traumatic events or in specific situations that remind you of trauma
- Physical reactions or panic attacks triggered by memories or reminders of the traumatic event

This checklist can be a starting point for recognizing the physical manifestations of trauma. It's important to note that having one or more of these symptoms does not necessarily mean you have experienced trauma - however, if these symptoms are persistent and significantly impact your quality of life, it might be beneficial to seek professional help. Consulting with a healthcare provider can also help determine the cause of these symptoms and develop an appropriate treatment plan.

In the realm of somatic therapy, developing an acute awareness of one's physical self is the foundation upon which the path to healing is built. This awareness guides us through the fog of disconnection that trauma often casts over the body. It is here, in the quiet observation of our physical sensations, that we begin to unlock the door to deeper understanding and, ultimately, transformation.

Starting the Journey

The initiation into body awareness is at once an exercise and a re-acquaintance with the self. For many, trauma creates a rift between the mind and body, leading to a life lived more in the head than in the flesh. This disconnection serves as a survival mechanism, a way to avoid the pain and discomfort that the body holds. However, it also keeps us from fully experiencing the present and can inhibit healing. By re-establishing this connection, by simply noticing, we start to mend the rift, acknowledging our physical selves with curiosity and without judgment.

Practical Exercises

Several exercises stand out for their effectiveness in cultivating body awareness. These practices invite us to slow down and tune into the whispers of our bodies:

- Mindful Breathing: This involves focusing on the breath, observing its rhythm, depth, and the sensations it creates in the body. It's an anchor to the present moment, drawing our attention away from the clutter of thoughts and into the physical self.

- Body Scanning: Lying down in a comfortable position, direct your attention gradually through each part of the body, from the toes to the top of the head. Notice sensations such as warmth, tightness, or tingling, without trying to change them. This scan illuminates areas of tension and relaxation, mapping the landscape of our physical selves.
- Sensory Engagement: Engage intentionally with the senses—touch, taste, sight, sound, and smell—to anchor in the present and cultivate an acute awareness of the body's interaction with its environment. This can be as simple as feeling the texture of fabric under your fingertips or noticing the nuances of flavor and texture in a bite of food.

Challenges and Strategies

As with any new skill, developing body awareness can present challenges. Some common hurdles include:

- Distraction: Our minds wander, pulled by thoughts of the past or future. When you notice your attention drifting, gently bring it back to the sensation you were focusing on, without self-criticism.
- Discomfort: Tuning into the body can sometimes reveal discomfort or pain, leading to avoidance. Approach these sensations with kindness, allowing them to be felt and heard. If they become overwhelming, shift your focus to a neutral part of

the body and return later, perhaps with a lesser intensity.

- Impatience: The desire for quick progress can lead to frustration. Remember, this is a process of relearning and reconnection that unfolds in its unique time.

To navigate these challenges, it helps to set realistic expectations through understanding that body awareness is a skill that deepens over time. Celebrate your small victories and progress! Furthermore, incorporating practices into your daily routine to make them part of your regular self-care will be very helpful. Consistency is key.

The Role of Patience and Persistence

Patience and persistence are vital allies on this journey. The road to reconnection with one's body is not linear; it is marked by ebbs and flows, moments of insight, and periods of seeming stillness. Each step forward, no matter how small, is a triumph, a reclaiming of territory long ignored or forgotten. It is through persistent, gentle attention that we begin to decode the language of our bodies, learning to inhabit ourselves fully once again. This process of cultivation, of patiently tending to our physical selves, allows for a blooming of awareness that can transform how we live and heal.

The Power of Breath: Breathing Techniques for Relaxation and Awareness

Within the moments of our lives that are stitched together by the rhythm of our breaths lies a simple yet profound tool for healing and awareness. Breathing, an act as natural as the ocean's tides, holds the key to calming the storm within us, gently guiding us back to tranquility and clarity.

This section illuminates the transformative potential of breath work, guiding you through techniques that not only soothe but also awaken a deeper connection with the self.

The Science of Breathing

The act of breathing does more than fill our lungs with air; it communicates with the nervous system, whispering signals of calm or alert depending on its pattern. When we engage in controlled breathing, we send a message to the nervous system to shift gears, moving from the often overactive sympathetic state to the calming embrace of the parasympathetic state. This transition is a crucial physiological recalibration that lowers heart rate, reduces blood pressure, and decreases stress hormone levels, leaving you in a state of peace and readiness for healing.

Breathing Exercises

Navigating through the landscape of breath work, we find a variety of exercises, each with its unique rhythm and purpose. Let's explore a few that have been proven time and again to promote relaxation and awareness:

- Diaphragmatic Breathing: By placing a hand on the abdomen and focusing on deep, slow breaths that expand the diaphragm rather than the chest, this technique encourages full oxygen exchange and engages the parasympathetic nervous system.
- 4-7-8 Breathing: Inhale through the nose for four counts, hold the breath for seven counts, and exhale

through the mouth for eight counts. This pattern, repeated for a few cycles, acts as a natural tranquilizer for the nervous system.

- Alternate Nostril Breathing: This is a practice borrowed from ancient yoga traditions, where you gently close one nostril, inhale through the other, and then switch nostrils for the exhale. This dance of breath balances the body's energy channels and harmonizes the hemispheres of the brain.

Incorporating Breathing into Daily Life

The beauty of breath work lies in its simplicity and accessibility, making it possible to include these practices into our daily routines. Here are three simple yet powerful ways to integrate mindful breathing into your day.

1. Morning Intentions: Begin your day with a few minutes of diaphragmatic breathing, setting a calm and centered tone for the hours ahead.

2. Transitional Breaths: Use moments of transition, such as finishing a task or arriving home, to practice a few cycles of 4-7-8 breathing, marking the end of one activity and the beginning of another with a clear, calm mind.

3. Mindful Moments: Throughout the day, take short "breath breaks," pausing for a minute or two of alternate nostril breathing, to reset and recharge, especially during moments of stress or fatigue.

The Benefits of Breath Work

The realm of breath work is rich with benefits that impact our emotional, physical, and mental well-being. For one thing, it offers a direct pathway to emotional regulation, soothing emotional turmoil, providing a tool to navigate anxiety, anger, and sadness with greater ease. There is also no doubt that it enhances physical health as, beyond immediate relaxation, regular breath work can improve respiratory function, invigorate circulation, and boost immune system resilience. Additionally, mindful breathing practices are known to sharpen mental clarity and focus. By calming the mind's chatter, breath work clears the mental fog, facilitating a state of presence and attentiveness.

In essence, the practice of controlled breathing serves as a bridge, connecting the islands of our existence - body, mind, and spirit - in a harmonious landscape. It reflects the body's inherent wisdom and capacity for self-regulation, a reminder that within each breath lies the potential for healing, transformation, and awakening. Let's remember the power of our breath, a gentle force that shapes our experience and existence, moment by moment, inhale through exhale.

Muscle Memory and Emotional Release: How Our Bodies Remember

Our muscles hold memories, encapsulating emotional experiences just as vividly as any thought or image our minds might conjure. This muscle memory isn't just about repetitive physical actions becoming second nature, but also our emotional history being written into the very fabric of our physical selves. When we experience trauma, our muscles contract, sometimes holding onto that tension long after the initial event has passed. This tension is a silent witness to our past, a holder of unspoken stories waiting to be acknowledged and released.

Exploring Muscle Memory

Muscle memory, in the context of trauma and emotional experiences, is an involuntary physical response to a feeling or memory. For instance, shoulders might tense up in situations that subconsciously remind us of a time when we felt burdened or stressed. This reaction is the body's way of preparing to deal with a perceived threat, a remnant of our instinctual fight or flight response. However, when these muscular reactions become chronic, they can lead to discomfort, pain, and even mobility issues, signaling a need for release.

The Process of Releasing

Techniques for releasing the emotional and physical tension stored in our muscles are varied, each offering a unique path to relief and healing. Here are a few of my favorites:

Massage

Deep tissue and therapeutic massage can help to loosen the tightness held in muscles, encouraging a release of both physical and emotional tension. What is incredibly special (and less often mentioned) when it comes to touch therapy or massages is that these practices often carry us into a state somewhere between wakefulness and sleep, which enhances the production of theta brain waves. This promotes a connection between our conscious and unconscious minds, which is a central aspect of shadow, inner child, and somatic healing.

Stretching

Gentle stretching exercises can increase flexibility and circulation, gradually easing the muscle's grip on past traumas. It also usually involves mindful breathing, which is an important part of releasing emotional blockages. Moreover, including this in your daily routine may allow you to systematically rest, ground, and regroup.

Movement

Activities that incorporate rhythm, such as drumming, dance, or even walking, can have a soothing effect on the nervous system. The predictability and structure of rhythmic movement can help regulate the body's stress response systems and promote a state of calm. Other activities like yoga, running, and tai chi allow for expressive movement that can unlock and release the emotional stories etched into our muscles. This is often where stress and trauma are physically held in the body. By engaging in movement, muscles can relax, reducing stiffness and pain, which can be physical manifestations of emotional stress.

Moreover, physical activity is well-known to influence the brain's chemistry by increasing the production of endorphins, which are chemicals that improve mood and reduce pain. Movement can also decrease the production of stress hormones like cortisol. This biochemical change can help alleviate both emotional and physical tension.

Through these three main techniques, we can develop outlets for emotional release and encourage our bodies to let go of the past. Doing more than alleviating physical discomfort, they offer an opportunity to acknowledge and honor our emotional histories by allowing them to surface and then move through us, leaving us lighter and more present.

The Importance of Safety and Trust

Creating a safe and trusting environment is crucial for the

process of releasing muscle memory. This safety can be physical, ensuring that the space in which we engage in these practices is comfortable and secure. More importantly, it must be emotional, fostering an atmosphere where vulnerability is met with compassion and understanding. Whether working with a therapist, a trusted instructor, or on our own, the feeling of being supported and safe in our explorations and expressions of stored trauma is vital. It is within this cocoon of security that true release and healing can occur, as the body and mind learn to trust in the process and in their capacity for resilience.

Transformative Effects

The effects of releasing muscle memory are profound, impacting both our emotional well-being and our physical health. Individuals often report a sense of lightness and liberation following the release of chronic muscular tension, describing it as a shedding of weight they didn't know they were carrying. Physically, the reduction in muscle tightness can lead to improved posture, increased mobility, and a decrease in pain and discomfort.

But the benefits extend beyond the physical. Emotionally, releasing muscle memory can lead to significant shifts in how we relate to our past traumas. By letting go of the physical reminders of our pain, we open ourselves up to a deeper level of healing, one that acknowledges the interconnectedness of body and mind. This process can lead to increased emotional resilience, a greater sense of peace, and a renewed capacity to engage with life in a more present and meaningful way.

IN ESSENCE, the act of releasing muscle memory is a powerful step toward reclaiming our bodies and our stories. It allows us to move forward, not by forgetting the past, but by integrating and transcending it. As we close this chapter, let's carry with us the understanding that our bodies are not just vessels for our existence but active participants in our healing journey. This realization opens the door to the next chapter of our exploration, where we continue to uncover the ways in which somatic therapy can illuminate the path to wholeness and peace.

THREE
MINDFUL AWARENESS THROUGH BODY SCANNING

I magine that you're sitting in a quiet room.

The only sound is the rhythm of your breath. You're about to listen to a symphony that's played not by instruments, but by your body. Sure, you will notice the obvious - a cramped neck from too much screen time or the soreness in your back from gardening yesterday. However, this precious moment is your chance to tune into your body's subtle cues: the warmth of your hands, the weight of your feet on the floor, perhaps even the flutter of your heartbeat.

This is the essence of body scanning, a practice that turns inward to explore the body's landscape, discovering its places of ease and tension. It's a method that invites us to meet ourselves right where we are, with kindness and curiosity.

Body Scanning: The Basics

Body scanning is essentially a mindfulness exercise that encourages us to pay meticulous attention to different parts of our body in a sequential manner, usually from head to toe or vice versa. It's about observing without the intention to change anything. Think of it as being a curious observer of your own body, noticing each part as if for the first time. This practice helps us tune into our bodily sensations, recognizing areas of tension, discomfort, or relaxation without judgment.

Origins and development

Drawing from ancient mindfulness traditions, body scanning has been an integral part of various healing and meditative practices for centuries. Its formal introduction into Western therapeutic practices is largely credited to Jon Kabat-Zinn and the Mindfulness-Based Stress Reduction (MBSR) program. Kabat-Zinn's work in integrating mindfulness into stress reduction and pain management has highlighted body scanning as a key tool for promoting deep bodily awareness and healing.

Benefits for healing

Engaging in body scanning offers numerous benefits, particularly in the realm of mental health and somatic therapy.

Stress Reduction: By focusing on the present moment and bodily sensations, body scanning can significantly lower stress levels, offering a peaceful break from the hustle of daily life. Pain Management: It provides insights into how pain is experienced in the body, often leading to a reduction in pain perception as one learns to observe discomfort with detachment. Emotional Release: As we become more attuned to our bodies, we might uncover emotional blockages manifested as physical tension, paving the way for emotional processing and release. Increased Body Awareness: Regular practice enhances our connection with our bodies, helping us recognize signs of stress or illness early on.

It's important to approach body scanning with a mindset open to whatever arises, without expecting instant relaxation or insights. Patience is key. Some days you might find the practice deeply calming; other days, it might feel challenging to stay focused. Both experiences are valuable. Body scanning is not about achieving a particular state but about cultivating an attitude of curiosity and non-judgment towards our bodily experiences.

Body Scanning Checklist

Engaging in a body scanning practice can be a deeply restorative and insightful experience, offering a moment to connect with oneself on a profound level. This checklist is designed to ensure you maximize the benefits of this practice.

Find a Quiet, Comfortable Space: Choose an environment where interruptions are minimal. This space should feel safe and serene to you, allowing for a sense of peace and the ability to focus without external distractions.

Choose Your Position Wisely: Your physical comfort is paramount in a body scanning session. Decide whether lying down, sitting, or slowly walking suits your current state and preference best. Each position offers a unique perspective and experience, so select the one that feels most conducive to introspection and relaxation.

Set a Gentle Intention: Before beginning, take a moment to mentally articulate your intention for the practice. This could be as simple as saying to yourself, "I am here to notice, not to fix." Such an intention sets a tone of non-judgment and openness, reminding you that the goal is to observe and be present with whatever arises.

Embrace a Patient Mindset: It's natural for the mind to wander during a body scanning practice. When you notice your thoughts drifting, gently acknowledge this without criticism and redirect your focus back to your body sensations. Remember, wandering thoughts are not failures but opportunities to practice patience and gently return to the moment.

By keeping this checklist in mind, you're setting the stage for a meaningful and enriching body scanning practice. Each step is designed to help you enter a state of deep awareness and connection with your body, enabling a profound exploration of the physical and emotional landscapes within.

Your Guide to Body Scanning

Body scanning involves paying attention to parts of the body and bodily sensations in a gradual sequence from feet to head. As you know, by tuning into your body, you can promote relaxation and enhance your mind-body connection. Just below is an overview of the body scanning process. Additionally, at the end of this book, you will find a beautiful guided body scan meditation.

Step-by-Step Flow

1. Find a Quiet Space: Choose a calm and comfortable setting where you won't be disturbed.
2. Choose Your Position: Lie down on your back or sit comfortably, ensuring your posture is relaxed yet attentive.
3. Breathe Deeply: Close your eyes and take several deep breaths, inhaling through your nose and exhaling through your mouth to settle into the moment.
4. Scan Your Body: Begin at your feet and slowly move your attention up through your body. Notice each part of your body from your toes to your head. Acknowledge any sensations, pain, or discomfort you might feel, without judgment. If you encounter areas of tension, imagine your breath flowing to these areas, gently enveloping them in warmth and care.
5. Acknowledge and Release: As you notice sensations, acknowledge them, and imagine each

breath flowing to and from that part of the body, releasing tension with each exhale.

6. Conclude Your Practice: Once you've scanned all the way to the top of your head, take a few more deep breaths and slowly open your eyes. Take a moment to notice how your body feels as a whole and carry that awareness with you.

TRYING a new method of tapping into your inner world can bring its lot of challenges. As you begin to include this practice into your regular self-care routine, please remember to:

- **Redirect**: When your mind wanders, acknowledge the distraction gently without judgment and guide your attention back to the body part you were focusing on.
- **Use Guided Recordings**: Especially in the beginning, following along with guided body scan meditations can help keep you on track.
- **Establish a Routine**: Practicing at the same time each day can help body scanning become a habit, making it easier to maintain focus.
- **Embrace Distractions**: Understand that distractions are part of the process. They're opportunities to practice returning your focus to the present.

Finally, by incorporating body scanning into your daily routine, you can enjoy the profound benefits it brings to both your mental and physical health. Whether you're new to mindfulness or looking to deepen your practice, body scanning is a simple yet powerful tool to enhance your overall well-being.

In a world brimming with constant stimulation, our bodies often whisper secrets of our deepest emotions and states of being, secrets that we, in our perpetual busyness, might over-look. These whispers, if listened to during a body scan, can reveal the tales of tension, discomfort, or even unexpected ease within us.

This section peels back the layers of our physical sensations to uncover what they might signify about our emotional well-being and how we might process and integrate these discoveries into our broader healing practices. Moreover, it sheds light on recognizing when additional support could be beneficial in navigating the sometimes-ravelled messages of our bodies.

Recognizing Physical Sensations

Throughout your body scan, a variety of sensations might come to the surface. Here's a look at some of the most common ones and their potential implications.

Tightness or Tension: Often found in the shoulders, neck, or back, tightness can signify stress or burden. It might indicate areas where we metaphorically "carry the weight of the world".

Warmth or Heat: Sensations of warmth, especially in the hands or chest, might reflect feelings of love, compassion, or healing.

Coldness or Numbness: Feeling cold or numb in certain body parts can sometimes point to avoidance or disconnection from certain emotions or experiences.

Fluttering or Tingling: These sensations, perhaps in the

stomach or limbs, might signal anticipation, anxiety, or the reawakening of parts of ourselves we've neglected.

By paying attention to these sensations without judgment, we can start to decode the body's language, gaining insights into our emotional landscapes.

Emotional Responses to Body Scanning

As we direct our attention inward during a body scan, we might encounter a spectrum of emotions. Discovering areas of relaxation can elicit feelings of relief, a sign of unburdening or letting go. Acknowledging areas of tension or discomfort can sometimes release pent-up emotions, leading to a sense of sadness as we connect with past hurts. Also, focusing on the body might initially heighten feelings of anxiety for some, especially if the body scan brings attention to previously ignored areas of tension.

These emotional responses are natural and valuable. They offer clues to our internal states, encouraging us to explore and heal underlying issues. When emotions surface, acknowledging them and allowing them to be present without forcing a change can be a powerful step in processing these feelings.

Making Sense of the Body's Messages

Interpreting the body's signals requires patience and openness, allowing for a nuanced understanding of our physical and emotional states. Here are some strategies for making sense of the body's messages.

Pattern Recognition: Over time, you might notice certain sensations recur under specific circumstances. Mapping these patterns can provide insights into how your body reacts to stress, joy, or other emotional states.

Emotion-Sensation Link: Try to connect physical sensations with emotional states. For instance, tightness in the chest might be linked to feelings of anxiety or sadness.

Mindful Reflection: After a body scan, spend a few moments reflecting on the experience. Consider journaling about the sensations and emotions observed, exploring their potential meanings and connections to your life.

When to Seek Further Guidance

While body scanning is a powerful tool for self-awareness and healing, there are instances when professional support can be invaluable. If certain physical sensations persistently cause discomfort or are linked to unexplained pain, consulting a healthcare provider or a somatic therapist can help address these issues more deeply. Should emotions become overwhelming or lead to distress, a mental health professional skilled in somatic practices can offer support, helping to navigate and process these feelings in a safe and structured environment. Furthermore, the desire to explore the body's messages more deeply or to integrate somatic practices into healing from trauma might prompt seeking a therapist.

Listening to our bodies through the practice of body scanning opens up a dialogue with ourselves that is both revealing and healing. It teaches us to meet our physical sensations and emotional responses with curiosity and compassion. As we learn to interpret and integrate these messages, we cultivate a more harmonious balance between body and mind, moving closer to a state of well-being that embraces the totality of our experiences.

Integrating Body Scans into Daily Life for Continuous Awareness

The essence of mindfulness lies not in the grand gestures of retreats or hour-long meditations but in weaving moments of awareness into our daily lives. This is particularly true with body scanning, a practice that, when integrated regularly, can become a touchstone for self-awareness and a means to gracefully navigate through the day's stresses and strains.

Making body scanning a part of your daily routine invites a constant stream of mindfulness into your life, transforming mundane moments into opportunities for self-discovery and stress relief. Consider the following to seamlessly include body scanning in your day.

Morning: Start your day by spending a few minutes in bed, conducting a brief body scan before rising. This can help set a tone of awareness and presence for the day ahead.

Work Breaks: Use short breaks at work to conduct mini body scans, even if it's just focusing on your hands, feet, or breath. These brief pauses can reduce stress and increase productivity by refocusing and re-energizing your mind.

Evening: End your day with a more thorough body scan, perhaps before sleep. This can aid in releasing the day's tensions and transitioning into restful sleep.

For those moments when time is scarce, short-form body scanning can be a powerful tool. These abbreviated versions focus on one part of the body or even just the breath and can be done anywhere, anytime. Here are two examples:

1. Hand Awareness: Focus on the sensations in your hands — the temperature, textures, and any tingling or pulsing. It's a simple yet effective way to ground yourself in the present.

2. Foot Grounding: Pay attention to your feet on the ground, feeling the solidity of the earth beneath you. This can be particularly calming in moments of anxiety or overwhelm.

Another important aspect of body scanning is that it can be particularly potent when applied to specific emotional states or situations. Here are some ways in which you can use it as a self-soothing technique:

- In stressful moments, a quick body scan can help identify areas of tension. Once recognized, directing your breath to these areas can facilitate relaxation and release.
- During anxious episodes, focusing on grounding parts of the body, like the feet or seat, can help stabilize your emotions, anchoring you back to a sense of safety.
- When emotions flood in, conducting a body scan with an emphasis on the heart and stomach (areas often affected by strong emotions) can help in acknowledging and gently navigating these feelings.

The beauty of integrating body scanning into daily routines lies in the cumulative effect it has on well-being. Consistency in practice deepens the connection with one's body, enhancing the ability to detect nuances of sensation and emotional states.

Enhanced Stress Management: Regular body scanning fosters a more resilient response to stress, enabling you to meet challenges with a calm and centered presence.

Improved Physical Well-being: By regularly tuning into the body, you're more likely to notice early signs of physical discomfort or illness, allowing for timely care and attention.

Deeper Emotional Insight: Continuous practice cultivates a nuanced understanding of how emotions manifest in the body, providing valuable insights for emotional processing and healing.

Increased Mindfulness: The habit of body scanning reinforces a broader mindfulness practice, encouraging a more attentive, present, and compassionate approach to life's experiences.

Through regular engagement, this practice becomes less of an activity and more of a way of being.

Challenges in Body Scanning: Common Obstacles and Solutions

Navigating through the practice of body scanning, one might encounter hurdles that can seem to obscure the path to deeper self-awareness and healing. Recognizing and addressing these challenges head-on is vital to maintaining a nourishing and effective practice.

Distraction and Restlessness

The mind's tendency to wander and the body's inclination towards restlessness can disrupt the flow of a body scan, making it difficult to maintain focus. Here are strategies to gently recalibrate your attention:

- Anchor in Sound: Incorporate ambient sounds or gentle music as a background to your practice. This auditory cue can help anchor your mind, providing a gentle return point for wandering thoughts.
- Guided Visualizations: Integrate visualizations into your body scan. Imagining a wave of light or warmth moving through your body can keep both mind and body engaged in the practice.
- Incremental Sessions: Start with shorter sessions, gradually increasing the duration as your concentration improves. This builds your focus muscle without overwhelming it.

Dealing with Discomfort or Emotional Pain

Body scanning can sometimes surface discomfort or emotional pain, which may deter one from continuing the practice. Here's how to navigate this:

- Gentle Acknowledgment: Recognize and acknowledge the discomfort or pain without forcing it away. This acceptance can often lessen its intensity.
- Shift the Focus: If certain areas bring significant discomfort, allow yourself to shift focus to a part of the body that feels neutral or pleasant, balancing the experience with positive sensations.
- Breathing Through: Use your breath as a tool to surround areas of discomfort with care. Imagine breathing into and out from the discomfort, envisioning a softening or release with each breath.

Building a Consistent Practice

Consistency is key to reaping the full benefits of body scanning, yet establishing a regular practice can be challenging. Here are tips to create a sustainable routine:

- Schedule It: Treat your body scanning time as you would any important appointment, scheduling it into your day with reminders to ensure it's a priority.
- Flexible Timing: Find the time of day that works best for you, whether it's morning to start your day centered or evening to unwind and reflect.
- Variety in Practice: Keep the practice fresh by varying your approach, perhaps trying different postures or integrating new visualization techniques.

IN CLOSING, let's carry these insights forward, recognizing that the practice of body scanning is but one element in the broader framework of somatic therapy. As we continue to explore somatics, remember that each practice and insight adds to the richness of your journey. Let's make sure we open ourselves to exploring new dimensions of this practice, with an eagerness to uncover the deeper connections and transformations that await.

FOUR
ANCHORING IN THE NOW

In somatic therapy, mindfulness guides us to experience our body and emotions in their purest form, without the weight of past traumas or future anxieties. The essence of mindfulness is a state of being fully present and engaged in the now, aware yet detached from judgment.

It is here, in the realm of the present, that healing finds fertile ground.

Mindfulness in Somatic Therapy: The Role of Present Moment Awareness

Mindfulness, at its core, is about paying attention. When applied to healing, it is a tool that brings us into direct contact with our experiences, allowing us to observe our physical sensations, thoughts, and emotions from a place of curiosity rather than judgment. This observational stance is crucial in somatic therapy. It shifts our focus from trying to "fix" what we perceive as problems to simply being with what is. This shift is transformative, offering a path to healing that embraces acceptance and presence, turning our attention to the richness of each moment and what it can teach us about ourselves.

Practices to Enhance Mindfulness

Integrating mindfulness into somatic therapy can take various forms, each inviting a deeper connection with the present moment.

Mindful Eating: This practice involves paying close attention to the process of eating—observing the colors, textures, and smells of food, chewing slowly, and noting the flavors and sensations in each bite. It turns a daily activity into an exercise in presence, promoting a greater appreciation for nourishment and the act of eating.

Mindful Walking: Here, walking becomes a deliberate act of mindfulness. Notice each step, the feel of the ground beneath your feet, the rhythm of your breath, and the sensations in your body as you move. It's a way to ground yourself in the now, turning a simple walk into a profound exercise in awareness.

Mindful Listening: Engage fully in the act of listening, whether to sounds in your environment or to another person. Notice the nuances in sounds, the rise and fall of voices, and the spaces between sounds. This practice cultivates a deep sense of presence and can enhance communication and relationships through authentic engagement.

The Benefits of a Mindful Approach

The inclusion of mindfulness in somatic therapy offers a range of benefits, touching every aspect of our being. These practices have been shown to lower levels of cortisol, the stress hormone, promoting a sense of calm and reducing anxiety. Regular mindfulness practice can also lower blood pressure, improve sleep, and enhance overall physical health and well-being.

Seeing mindfulness as more than just a series of practices - as a way of life - can transform our relationship with our body and emotions. It invites us to approach every moment with freshness and curiosity, whether we're washing dishes, taking a shower, or simply breathing. This attitude of presence enriches our daily experiences, turning routine activities into opportunities for discovery and connection. It's a way of moving through life where each step, each breath, is an act of mindfulness, bringing us closer to the essence of who we are.

Mindfulness Integration Checklist

Setting Intentions

- Reflect on your current state: Take a moment to note how you're feeling physically, emotionally, and mentally.
- Set a clear intention for your mindfulness practice today: Consider what you wish to cultivate or release (e.g., peace, clarity, healing of emotional pain).
- Write down your intention: Keep it somewhere you can see throughout the day to remind you of your focus.

Choosing Mindfulness Practices

Mark the practices you feel drawn to and would like to incorporate into your daily routine.

o **Breath Awareness:** Dedicate 5-10 minutes to observe your breath, noting the rise and fall of your chest or the sensation of air at your nostrils.

o **Body Scan:** Spend 10-15 minutes scanning through each part of your body, observing without judgment any sensations, tensions, or emotions that arise.

o **Walking Meditation:** Incorporate a 10-20 minute mindful walk into your day, paying attention to the sensation of each step and the environment around you.

o **Mindful Eating:** Choose one meal or snack to eat mindfully, observing the flavors, textures, and sensations of eating without distraction.

o **Journaling:** Spend 5-10 minutes writing about your experiences, thoughts, and feelings during your mindfulness practices or throughout the day.

Daily Practice Schedule

Schedule a consistent time for your mindfulness practice, or a combination that suits your lifestyle:

o Morning
o Midday
o Evening
o Other: _____

Set Gentle Reminders:

o Sticky notes
o Phone alarms or Apps to remind you of your practice times
o Other: _____

Approaching Activities with Curiosity and Non-Judgment

- Embrace a beginner's mind: Approach each practice as if it's your first time, even if it's familiar.
- Notice judgment and let it go: When you catch yourself judging your experience or progress, acknowledge it and then return to your practice without self-criticism.
- Cultivate curiosity: Each day, try to notice something new in your practice or how it affects you differently.

Reflection and Adjustment

- Weekly reflection: Spend 10-15 minutes at the end of the week reviewing your journal entries and experiences. What did you learn? What surprised you?
- Adjust practices as needed: Based on your reflection, decide if you need to try different practices, adjust the time spent, or focus on different intentions.
- Celebrate progress: Acknowledge your commitment to your practice and any shifts you've noticed in your well-being, no matter how small.

Additional Tips:

1. If possible, designate a quiet and comfortable area in your home for mindfulness practices.
2. Consider connecting with a mindfulness group or online community for support and shared experiences.
3. Be patient and kind with yourself: Remember that mindfulness is a practice, not a destination. Some days will be easier than others, and that's perfectly okay.

If possible, keep your checklist in a visible place to guide and remind you of your journey toward integrating mindfulness into your daily life. Adjust it as you go along to fit your evolving needs and preferences.

Mindful Moment Prompts

Incorporate these Mindful Moment Prompts into your day to cultivate a continuous practice of mindfulness, enhancing your somatic and shadow work. Each prompt is designed to be a gentle nudge back to the present moment, helping you create a deeper connection with your inner self and the world around you. Whether you're new to mindfulness or looking to deepen your practice, these simple activities can be seamlessly integrated into your daily life.

Prompts for Spontaneous Mindfulness:

One-Minute Breath Focus: Pause for one minute, close your eyes if possible, and focus solely on your breath. Notice the sensation of air entering and exiting your nostrils, and observe the rise and fall of your chest.

Sensory Engagement with Your Morning Beverage: While drinking your morning coffee or tea, engage all your senses. Observe its color, smell its aroma, feel the warmth of the cup, and taste each sip. Be fully present in the experience.

Mindful Listening: Spend a few minutes listening to the sounds around you, whether you're indoors or outdoors. Try to identify as many sounds as you can, listening without judgment or analysis.

Gratitude Touch Points: Identify three things you're grateful for at this moment. They can be as simple as the sunlight streaming through a window, a comfortable chair, or having a meal. Feel the gratitude in your heart.

Mindful Movement Stretch: Stand up and engage in a slow, mindful stretch. Pay attention to the sensations in your muscles and joints. Breathe deeply and notice how your body feels during and after the stretch.

Texture Exploration: Touch something nearby and focus on its texture. It could be the fabric of your clothes, the surface of your desk, or a natural object like a plant. Notice the details with your fingertips.

Aroma Awareness: Take a moment to notice any smells in your environment. If you have a fragrance source nearby, like a flower or a cup of coffee, close your eyes and take a deep inhale, fully experiencing the aroma.

Visual Mindfulness: Look around you and choose an object to focus on for a few moments. Observe it as if you're seeing it for the first time, noticing its colors, shapes, and any details you might usually overlook.

Mindful Eating Snack: Choose a small snack and eat it mindfully. Pay attention to the process of chewing and the flavors and textures of the food. How does it feel in your mouth? What sensations do you notice?

Heartbeat Check-In: Place your hand over your heart and focus on your heartbeat for a few moments. Feel the rhythm and notice any sensations in your body. Use this time to connect with yourself.

How to Use These Prompts

1. Set random alarms throughout the day as prompts for a

mindful moment. When the alarm goes off, choose one to practice.

2. Use a prompt as a transition between tasks or activities to reset and refocus your attention.

3. Share a prompt with a friend, family member, or coworker, and practice together, either in person or virtually, to deepen the sense of connection and presence.

Incorporating these Mindful Moment Prompts into your daily life can serve as a powerful tool in your somatic healing and shadow work journey, offering regular opportunities to reconnect with the present.

Grounding Techniques: Staying Anchored During Emotional Storms

In navigating the highs and lows of emotional experiences, grounding emerges as a foundation for stability. Imagine yourself in the midst of an emotional tempest, where thoughts and feelings whirl around with dizzying intensity. Grounding is the anchor that helps you find your footing, offering a return to a place of calm and clarity. It's a practice rooted in the present, a deliberate focus on the here and now that can dissipate the fog of overwhelm, anxiety, or dissociation.

Grounding is particularly effective because it shifts your focus from the storm of internal experiences to the solid reality of the external world. This transition is not about ignoring emotions but providing a safe platform from which to observe and manage them.

The beauty of grounding lies in its simplicity and accessibility. Here are exercises that can be woven into any moment, requiring nothing more than your intention and attention.

5-4-3-2-1 Technique: Engage all five senses to bring your awareness into the present. Identify five things you can see, four you can touch, three you can hear, two you can smell, and one you can taste. This practice is especially useful for halting the spiral of anxious thoughts and rooting yourself in the environment around you.

Focused Object Observation: Choose any object in your vicinity—a pen, a cup, a plant—and spend a few minutes observing it in detail. Notice its color, texture, weight, and any other characteristics. This concentration on a single point draws your attention away from distressing emotions and into a state of focused calm.

Grounding Through Movement: Simple movements like stretching your arms, gripping your chair, or slowly tapping your feet on the ground can help reconnect with your body and the physical space you occupy. Movement acts as a gentle reminder of your physical presence in the world, anchoring you firmly to the present.

The Role of the Senses

Utilizing the five senses is a cornerstone of effective grounding techniques. Sensory experiences provide immediate, tangible points of focus that can easily be accessed at any moment. Here's how each sense can play a role in grounding:

Sight: Observing the details in your environment or focusing on a specific color can redirect your attention outward.

Touch: Feeling the texture of an object, the fabric of your clothes, or the ground beneath your feet can help you reconnect with the present.

Hearing: Listening to ambient sounds, music, or your own breathing can calm the mind and reduce feelings of anxiety.

Smell: Inhaling a comforting scent, whether from a cup of tea, a scented candle, or fresh air, can have an immediate soothing effect.

Taste: Savoring a piece of fruit, a mint, or even a sip of water can be a simple yet effective way to ground yourself.

Personalizing Grounding Practices

While grounding techniques share the common goal of returning you to a state of calm, their effectiveness can vary from person to person. Personalizing your approach ensures that your grounding practices resonate with your needs and preferences. Here are four elements to consider when tailoring your practice to reflect your individuality.

1. Experiment with Different Techniques: Explore a variety of grounding exercises to discover which ones feel most effective for you. You might find that certain practices work better in specific situations or that your preferences change over time.
2. Create a Grounding Plan: Once you've identified the techniques that work best for you, create a personalized grounding plan. This plan can include a list of preferred exercises and when to use them, such as specific techniques for quick

grounding in public spaces or more involved practices for deeper emotional work at home.

3. Incorporate Grounding into Your Routine: Look for opportunities to integrate grounding exercises into your daily routine. This could mean starting your day with a grounding meditation, using focused object observation during work breaks, or ending your day with a sensory grounding practice.

4. Adapt and Adjust: Be open to adjusting your grounding practices as your needs evolve. What works for you today might change, and that's okay. The key is to stay attuned to your body and emotions, adapting your techniques to support your well-being in the moment.

Grounding stands as a testament to the power of presence, a practice that gently but firmly guides you back to a place of stability and clarity amidst emotional chaos. Through focused attention on the present and the deliberate engagement of the senses, grounding techniques create tranquility and balance, accessible anytime and anywhere.

Breathing as Grounding: Simple Yet Effective Techniques

Within our daily lives, as every moment flows into the next, breath stands as a constant companion, a silent witness to our experiences. This act of breathing, so innate and automatic, hides within it a potent tool for grounding and calming. Through breathwork, we tap into this wellspring of tranquility, guiding our nervous system back to a state of balance and presence.

Here, we will explore the foundational aspects of using breath as a primary resource for grounding, along with practical exercises and the integration of mindfulness to enhance the practice. We will also uncover the science that underscores the efficacy of breathwork in somatic therapy, shedding light on how something as simple as breathing can be transformative.

Breathwork Basics

At its heart, breathwork involves conscious control over our breathing patterns to influence our mental, emotional, and physical states. It's a bridge connecting the conscious with the subconscious, the body with the mind, leading us to a place of deeper self-awareness and calm. As we discovered in previous chapters, by focusing on and manipulating our breath, we can signal our nervous system to shift from a state of alertness to one of relaxation, a transition that is both subtle and profound.

To begin, let's consider two foundational aspects of breathwork:

1. Observation: Start by simply observing your breath without any intention to change it. Notice its rhythm, depth, and the sensations it evokes in your body. This awareness is the first step toward harnessing the power of your breath.
2. Regulation: Once you're attuned to your natural breathing pattern, you can start experimenting with regulating your breath. This might involve deepening your inhales and exhales, introducing pauses, or finding a rhythm that feels soothing and grounding.

Guided Breathing Exercises

Engaging in guided breathing exercises can dramatically

enhance your ability to ground and center yourself. Here are a few techniques to try:

- Equal Breathing: Inhale slowly through your nose for a count of four, then exhale through your nose for the same count. This balanced breathing helps harmonize the nervous system.
- Box Breathing: Visualize a box as you breathe in for a count of four, hold your breath for four, exhale for four, and hold again for four. This practice is excellent for moments when you need to reset and focus.
- Progressive Relaxation Breath: Inhale deeply, filling your lungs completely. As you exhale, consciously release tension from your body, starting from your head and moving down to your toes. With each breath, feel yourself becoming more relaxed and grounded.

Integrating Breathwork with Mindfulness

Combining breathwork with mindfulness practices amplifies the grounding effect, creating a holistic approach to calming the mind and body. Here are ways to integrate these practices.

Mindful Awareness of Breath: As you engage in breathwork, bring a mindful awareness to the experience, noticing the sensations of air moving in and out of your body, the rise and fall of your chest, and any thoughts or emotions that arise, observing them without attachment.

Breathing in Nature: If you have access to an outdoor space, try practicing your breathwork surrounded by nature. The fresh air and natural beauty enhance mindfulness and the grounding effect of your breathwork.

Incorporating Mindful Pauses: Throughout your day, take short "breath breaks" to practice mindfulness and breathwork simultaneously. Even a few deep, mindful breaths can serve as a powerful grounding technique in the midst of a hectic schedule.

The Science Behind Breathwork

The transformative power of breathwork is not just a matter of subjective experience; it is grounded in science. When we engage in controlled breathing, we directly impact our autonomic nervous system, which regulates our stress response. Research has shown that breathwork can:

- Activate the Parasympathetic Nervous System: Slow, deep breathing activates the vagus nerve, a key component of the parasympathetic nervous system, signaling the body to relax and de-escalate the stress response.
- Reduce Cortisol Levels: Regular breathwork practice has been linked to lower levels of cortisol, the body's primary stress hormone, contributing to a state of calm and reducing anxiety.
- Enhance Brain Function: Controlled breathing can increase coherence between different parts of the brain, improving focus, emotional regulation, and cognitive performance.
- Improve Respiratory and Cardiovascular Health: By optimizing our breathing patterns, we can

enhance oxygen exchange, lower blood pressure, and improve overall cardiovascular health.

Breathwork, with its roots in ancient practices and its efficacy validated by modern science, creates a profound connection between breath, body, and mind. Through the simple act of breathing with intention, we can access a state of grounded presence, finding calm in the midst of chaos and clarity within complexity.

Nature as a Healer: Using Outdoor Spaces for Grounding

The natural world has long been recognized for its restorative properties, offering a sanctuary where the mind and body can find balance and peace. Recent studies underscore the profound impact that immersion in nature has on our well-being, highlighting reductions in stress, enhanced mood, and even improved cognitive function. This connection to the earth underpins many grounding practices, providing a powerful antidote to the disconnection and overstimulation of modern life.

The Therapeutic Effects of Nature

Within the canopy of a forest or the expanse of a desert, nature engages us in a dialogue that transcends words, speaking directly to our primal selves. The simple act of being in natural surroundings can lower blood pressure, decrease levels of cortisol, and elevate our mood. This is not merely anecdotal; research in the field of ecotherapy provides compelling evidence of these effects. For instance, a study published in the "International Journal of Environmental Research and Public Health" found that participants who engaged in walks within green spaces reported significantly lower stress levels and improved mental health outcomes compared to those in urban settings.

Practical Ways to Connect with Nature

Engaging with the natural world doesn't require grand adventures; even small acts can deepen our connection to the earth and its rhythms.

- Forest Bathing: Originating from Japan, forest bathing, or Shinrin-yoku, involves immersive walks in forested areas, focusing on the sensory experiences the environment offers.
- Gardening: Tending to plants, whether in a backyard garden or a container garden on a balcony, can be a meditative practice, fostering a sense of care and connection to the cycle of life.
- Nature Walks in Urban Parks: For those in urban environments, local parks offer green spaces for leisurely walks or simply sitting and observing nature's nuances.
- Beach Combing or River Walking: This is my absolute favorite. If you're near water, walking along a beach or riverbank provides a rhythmic, meditative experience, enhanced by the calming presence of water.

Overcoming Barriers to Outdoor Access

Access to natural spaces can be limited by urban living, mobility issues, or time constraints. However, with creativity, the benefits of nature can still be found.

- Indoor Plants and Herb Gardens: Bringing nature indoors through houseplants or a small herb garden can offer daily touchpoints with the natural world.
- Virtual Nature Experiences: Technology offers virtual walks through forests, mountains, and beaches, providing visual and auditory experiences of nature.
- Natural Elements in Home Decor: Incorporating elements like wood, stones, or water features into home décor can create a more natural, grounding environment.
- Nature Sounds: Listening to recordings of nature sounds, such as rain, birdsong, or ocean waves, can have a soothing, grounding effect, especially when outdoor access is challenging.

Nature-Inspired Mindfulness Practices

Incorporating mindfulness into outdoor activities amplifies the grounding effects of nature, creating a synergy that enhances both practices.

Mindful Observation: Choose an outdoor spot and spend time observing the details around you—the shape of leaves, the pattern of bark on a tree, the way light filters through branches. This focused observation brings you into the present moment, deepening your connection to the environment.

Sensory Walks: On a walk, engage each of your senses sequentially to fully experience your surroundings. Note what you see, then focus on what you can hear, followed by what you can smell, and finally, what you can feel. This practice not only grounds you but also enriches your experience of nature.

Breathing with Nature: Find a quiet spot outdoors to sit comfortably. Close your eyes and synchronize your breathing with the natural sounds around you, such as the wind or waves. This harmonization of your breath with the rhythms of nature fosters a deep sense of peace and belonging.

Gratitude Moments: While in nature, take a few moments to reflect on what you're grateful for, focusing on the elements of the natural world that nurture and sustain us. This gratitude practice not only grounds you but also fosters a positive, appreciative mindset.

Reconnecting with nature grounds us and rekindles our sense of wonder, reminding us of the beauty that surrounds us and resides within. Through intentional engagement with the outdoors—whether by immersing ourselves in forest canopies, tending to plants, or simply pausing to breathe in sync with the natural world—we can rediscover our intrinsic connection to the earth.

Building a Personal Toolkit: Customizing Techniques for Your Needs

Navigating mindfulness and grounding techniques can feel like standing at the edge of an ocean, contemplating its depth and expanse. The key is not to plunge into its depths all at once but to wade in gently, selecting the practices that resonate with your unique rhythm and flow. This process of selection and customization lies at the heart of creating a personal toolkit that aligns with your needs and preferences whilst evolving with you over time.

Assessing Personal Needs and Preferences

Initiating this process begins with a reflection on your current state and what you hope to achieve through mindfulness and grounding practices. Consider your daily routine, the challenges you face, and where you feel most disconnected. Are you seeking calm in a storm of anxiety? Or perhaps looking for moments of clarity amid confusion? Understanding these needs provides a compass for selecting practices that truly resonate with you.

Next, explore your preferences. Do you find solace in silence or comfort in the rhythmic sounds of nature? Does your body crave movement, or do you prefer stillness? If you're like me, you may find that every day your body requests something different. These questions are not meant to confine but to guide you towards practices that feel nurturing and right for you. So, listen to what your body is telling you and allow your intuition to show you the way.

Creating a Personalized Toolkit

Once you've gained a clearer understanding of your needs and preferences, it'll be time to assemble your toolkit. This process is both creative and intuitive, encouraging you to listen deeply to yourself and choose practices that feel like a balm to your soul. Here's a three-step framework to get you started.

First, from the list of mindfulness practices you've been introduced to, select two or three that you feel drawn to. This could be anything from mindful eating to focused object observation.

Next, choose a couple of grounding exercises that you feel will be most beneficial, especially in moments of emotional overwhelm. This could include the 5-4-3-2-1 technique or focused object observation.

Finally, incorporate one or two breathing exercises that you can call upon to center yourself. Equal breathing and box breathing are excellent places to start.

Remember, this toolkit is not static but a living collection that grows and changes as you do. Record any adjustments you make in your journal.

Flexibility and Adaptation

Staying open to experimentation is vital in this journey. As you practice, you might find that certain techniques don't resonate as you thought they would, or you may stumble upon new ones that feel like a perfect fit. This fluidity is natural and it is even encouraged. It reflects your growth and deepening understanding of yourself. Periodically review your toolkit, adding new techniques that you discover and letting go of those that no longer serve you.

Sharing and Community

While the practice of mindfulness and grounding is deeply personal, sharing your experiences and techniques with others can enrich your journey. It creates a space for mutual learning and support, offering new perspectives and insights.

Again, you may want to consider joining a mindfulness group or participating in forums where you can exchange ideas and practices. Also, teaching a friend or family member a technique that has been particularly impactful for you not only deepens your understanding but also fosters a shared experience of growth and healing. This exchange of knowledge and experience with others will broaden your own practice and contribute to a collective well-being.

As we conclude this exploration of building a personalized toolkit, remember that the essence of this process lies in tuning into your inner space, selecting practices that nurture and support you, and remaining open to the journey of discovery as it unfolds.

. . .

Now, let's turn our gaze to the next chapter, where we delve into the transformative world of trauma release through movement. Here, we will explore how the body, when given the freedom to express and move, can unlock pathways to healing that words alone cannot reach.

FIVE

REDISCOVERING BALANCE THROUGH MOVEMENT

Here you are.

Standing in the middle of a room, feeling the weight of the world on your shoulders.

Slowly, you begin to sway gently from side to side. With each movement, the weight begins to lift, leaving a sense of freedom in its wake.

I'm not just talking about physical motion. Movement is powerful - it can stir the stagnant parts of our lives, bringing a fresh flow of energy and emotion.

In this chapter, we will explore movement as a powerful tool for healing, offering a path to release trauma and restore emotional balance.

Movement as Medicine

From the moment we wake, our bodies are in constant motion, a silent language expressing our inner states. When words fall short, our bodies speak volumes. Movement therapy taps into this language, using physical activity to address and heal emotional pain. This is a process that acknowledges the body's role in storing and releasing trauma. Think of it like this: just as laughter can be a release valve for stress, physical movement offers a way to release emotional tension, transforming it into something manageable, even healing.

Varieties of Therapeutic Movement

Movement therapy encompasses a broad spectrum of activities, each with unique benefits. A few popular ones are yoga, dance, and martial arts. More than just poses and choreographies, these activities offer a mindful practice that connects breath with movement, promoting self-awareness and inner calm. They assist in freeing the body to express what's within, whether it's joy, sorrow, or something in between. Some combine slow, deliberate movements with deep breathing, enhancing physical and mental balance.

The Science Behind Movement Therapy

Recent studies shed light on how movement affects our brains and bodies, especially concerning trauma. One key finding is that physical activity, especially rhythmic, repetitive motions, can help regulate the nervous system, disrupted by traumatic experiences. Movement therapy has been shown to decrease symptoms of anxiety and depression, improve sleep, and even enhance cognitive functions like memory and attention. The body's physical movement can help "reprogram" the brain's response to stress, creating new pathways to emotional resilience.

Movement in Daily Life

Integrating therapeutic movement into your routine doesn't have to mean a complete overhaul of your day. Small shifts can lead to significant benefits. Here are some suggestions:

1. Morning Stretch: Begin your day by stretching your body, reaching your arms above your head, and gently swaying from side to side. It's a simple way to wake up your body and mind.
2. Walks: Take short walks during breaks at work or in the evening. Focus on the sensation of your feet touching the ground and the rhythm of your steps.
3. Breath and Movement: Pair deep breathing with simple movements like arm raises or shoulder rolls. It's a quick way to center yourself, especially during stressful moments.

Types of Therapeutic Movement and Their Benefits

The following are various movement activities used for somatic healing. This table highlights the key benefits of each activity so that you can explore and find the type that best resonates with your healing needs.

Type of Movement	Key Benefits
Yoga	- Stress relief - Improved flexibility and balance - Enhanced mental clarity and calmness
Dance	- Improved mood and emotional regulation - Increased physical fitness - Enhanced creativity
Martial Arts	- Enhanced focus and discipline - Improved physical strength and coordination - Stress reduction
Tai Chi	- Reduced anxiety and depression - Improved balance and motor function - Enhanced mindfulness and relaxation
Pilates	- Strengthened core muscles - Improved posture and alignment - Increased body awareness
Swimming	- Low-impact whole-body workout - Improved cardiovascular health - Relaxation and stress relief
Walking/ Nature Walks	- Enhanced mood through exposure to nature - Improved cardiovascular health - Stress relief and mental clarity
Cycling	- Increased physical endurance - Stress relief - Improved joint mobility and flexibility

Remember to choose activities that most resonate with you. These can sometimes be challenging, but they should always feel fulfilling and beneficial to your physical and mental well-being.

Create a Personalized Daily Movement Plan

Creating a personalized daily movement plan is a great way to incorporate physical activity into your routine in a way that feels enjoyable and sustainable. You can track your routines and record any emotional/physical changes or insights in your journal or movement diary. Here's a step-by-step guide to help you get started.

Step 1: Identifying Preferences

Explore Different Types of Movement: Experiment with various activities to find what you enjoy. This could include dance, yoga, martial arts, walking, cycling, or swimming. Pay attention to how each activity makes you feel during and after.

Listen to Your Body: Notice which movements feel good and which do not. Your preferences might change daily based on your body's needs, so stay flexible in your approach.

Consider Accessibility: Think about what activities are most accessible to you based on your current lifestyle, location, and resources. Choosing activities that are easy to incorporate into your life will increase your chances of sticking with them.

Step 2: Setting Realistic Goals

Assess Your Schedule: Look at your daily and weekly schedule to determine how much time you realistically have to dedicate to movement. It's better to start with a small, manageable goals.

Set Clear, Achievable Goals: Decide on specific, realistic goals. This could be as simple as dedicating 5 minutes each morning to stretching or taking a 15-minute walk during your lunch break.

Be Flexible: Allow for flexibility in your goals. If a 15-minute walk is too much some days, consider a shorter duration or a different activity that feels more doable.

Step 3: Integrating Movement into Your Routine

Identify Opportunities for Movement: Look for pockets of time in your routine where movement can fit naturally. This might include walking or biking to work, stretching while watching TV, or doing yoga before bed.

Make It Convenient: Prepare for your chosen activities in advance. If you plan to walk during lunch, consider keeping a pair of comfortable shoes at your workplace. If you enjoy yoga, set up a quiet, comfortable space in your home.

Track Your Progress: Keep a log of your activities and how they make you feel. This can help you adjust your plan based on what works best for you and provide motivation to keep going.

Be Consistent but Kind to Yourself: Aim for consistency in your movement plan, but be kind to yourself on days when it doesn't happen. The goal is to build a positive, sustainable relationship with movement.

Step 4: Review and Adjust

Evaluate Your Plan Regularly: Every few weeks, take some time to review your movement plan. Assess what's working and what isn't, and adjust your activities and goals as needed.

Seek Inspiration: Stay motivated by trying new types of movement, joining community classes, or partnering with a friend for joint activities.

By FOLLOWING THESE STEPS, you can create a personalized daily movement plan that fits your preferences, goals, and lifestyle. This will help you to enjoy the benefits of physical activity in a way that feels right for you and that promotes somatic healing through emotional regulation and release.

Yoga for Somatic Healing: Poses and Practices

Yoga, with its ancient roots, offers a unique blend of physical postures, breath control, and meditation that specifically caters to healing both the mind and body. It stands out in somatic therapy for its gentle approach to unraveling the layers of trauma stored within our bodies.

Through mindful movement and focused breathing, yoga invites a dialogue between the body and mind, facilitating a release of deeply rooted tensions and promoting a state of balanced well-being.

Yoga's Role in Somatic Therapy

At the heart of yoga's integration into somatic therapy is its ability to cultivate an increased body awareness. This awareness is critical in identifying and subsequently releasing the physical manifestations of emotional trauma. For instance, a forward bend does not merely stretch the hamstrings and lower back but also offers an opportunity to bow down, symbolically letting go of burdens. In this way, yoga postures, or asanas, serve as metaphors for emotional states, providing a safe space for us to explore and express feelings that might be difficult to articulate verbally.

Yoga also emphasizes staying present during practice, which can help break free from the grip of past traumas and anxieties about the future. This presence—anchored in each breath and movement—allows for a deeper connection with the self and healing from within.

Guided Yoga Sequences

For those seeking to release trauma and regulate emotions through yoga, specific sequences can be particularly beneficial.

Restorative Yoga Sequence

This involves a series of poses held for longer durations

with the support of props like blankets and bolsters. The aim is to create a physical and mental state of relaxation, allowing the body to release tension naturally. Poses such as Supported Child's Pose and Legs-Up-The-Wall encourage a gentle opening and relaxation of the body's stress points.

Gentle Flow Sequence

A series of fluid movements synchronized with the breath, designed to build a gentle heat in the body and encourage emotional release. Cat-Cow stretches, for example, promote spinal flexibility while facilitating an emotional connection with the heart and belly, areas often affected by trauma.

Breath and Movement Synergy

Integrating breathwork with yoga poses amplifies their healing potential. Each inhale in yoga can symbolize an acceptance and opening up to new experiences, while each exhale represents a release of what no longer serves us. For instance, in a pose like Warrior II, a deep inhale helps to expand the chest and open the heart, embodying courage and strength, whereas the exhale aids in grounding and stabilization. This synergy between breath and movement not only deepens the practice but also teaches individuals how to regulate their emotional responses, promoting resilience and emotional flexibility.

Adapting Yoga for All Bodies

Yoga is not a one-size-fits-all practice. It honors the uniqueness of each body and its capabilities. Here are ways to ensure yoga remains accessible and beneficial for everyone:

1. Modifications: Use props like blocks, straps, and chairs to modify poses, making them accessible for individuals with physical limitations or those new to yoga. For example, a block can bring the ground closer in a forward fold, reducing strain on the back and hamstrings.

2. Chair Yoga: This form of yoga is performed with the aid of a chair, either by sitting on it or using it for support in standing poses. It is ideal for those of us with mobility issues or seniors, allowing everyone to experience the benefits of yoga without having to get down on the floor.

3. Personalized Sequences: Tailoring yoga sequences to meet your individual needs can be extremely beneficial, especially if you are dealing with specific traumas or health conditions. A personalized approach ensures the practice addresses our unique healing journey, creating a sense of safety and progression.

Yoga's integration into somatic healing underscores the profound connection between our physical postures and emotional well-being. Through mindful practice, yoga allows us to explore the depths of our being, releasing the emotional blockages that inhibit our growth, embracing the present moment and a future where we are free to move and live without the weight of our past experiences.

Dancing Out Trauma: How Rhythmic Movement Can Heal

Within therapeutic practices, dance therapy emerges as a game changing healing method. Through combining rhythmic patterns of movement with the emotional landscape of the self, this form of therapy transcends conventional boundaries, allowing for a profound expression and processing of emotions through the body's natural movements. At its core, dance therapy acknowledges that our bodies hold stories and traumas that words alone cannot fully capture or release. Through dance, individuals are invited to communicate these narratives, engaging in a physical dialogue that drives emotional liberation.

Dance Therapy Fundamentals

Dance therapy, grounded in the principle that body and mind are interrelated, utilizes movement as a means of achieving emotional, cognitive, physical, and social integration. It operates on the understanding that changes in movement can affect total functioning, facilitating a pathway to discover, explore, and express one's deepest concerns and feelings. Certified dance therapists guide participants through this journey, employing both structured and improvised dance activities designed to mirror or express emotions, thus promoting insight, integration, and recovery.

Structured vs. Freeform Dance

The spectrum of dance therapy encompasses both structured and freeform dance, each offering unique benefits.

Structured dance involves specific choreography or sequences that aim to target certain emotions or physical states. This format can provide a sense of safety and containment for individuals, offering clear guidance and a structured outlet for expression. It can be particularly helpful for those who may feel overwhelmed by the openness of freeform dance, providing a scaffolded approach to exploring movement and emotion.

Freeform or intuitive dance encourages spontaneous movement, guided by the individual's internal rhythms and emotions. This unscripted approach allows for a direct and unfiltered expression of feelings, fostering a deep sense of freedom and personal exploration. It can be especially transformative for those feeling restricted or confined by their trauma, offering a space to explore and release emotions without the constraints of specific steps or patterns.

Both approaches to dance therapy play a crucial role in somatic healing, allowing us to choose the path that best aligns with our needs and comfort levels.

Creating a Safe Space for Dance

For dance therapy to be effective, creating a supportive and judgment-free environment is paramount. Such a space encourages participants to fully engage with their emotions and movements without fear of critique or embarrassment.

Here are some key considerations to create a positive and effective environment:

- Physical Safety: Ensure the space is free from obstacles and hazards, providing ample room for movement. Comfortable flooring and a private or semi-private setting can make us feel more at ease to express ourselves freely.
- Emotional Safety: Establish ground rules that emphasize respect, confidentiality, and non-judgment. Encouraging an atmosphere of openness and empathy allows us to feel supported and understood.
- Guidance and Support: Having a skilled facilitator or therapist present to guide the session and provide emotional support is quite important.

Their role is to guide and support us through the process, usually by offering prompts or interventions as needed, while ensuring a safe emotional space for all.

Shaking and Vibrational Practices

In the realm of healing, the practice of shaking and vibrational movements emerges as a profound method to address and release the physical manifestations of trauma embedded within our bodies. This method, both ancient and modern, serves as a powerful means to liberate those often ineffable emotions held in our physical form, facilitating a process of renewal and release.

Cultural and Historical Context

The use of shaking as a form of emotional release and healing is a concept deeply rooted in various cultures around the world. Many indigenous traditions recognize the therapeutic value of rhythmic movement and vibration, incorporating them into rituals and ceremonies aimed at physical and emotional purification. For example, the Kalahari Bushmen of Africa engage in trance dances, where intense shaking is a key component, believed to activate healing energies and foster community connection. Similarly, in the practices of Qigong and Tai Chi from China, subtle vibrations and shaking movements are used to unblock energy pathways and promote health.

The Science of Shaking

Shaking practices, when examined through the lens of physiology and psychology, reveal a fascinating interplay between our physical actions and emotional states. The act of shaking or engaging in vibrational movements activates the body's natural relaxation response, a counterbalance to the fight-or-flight mechanism triggered by stress or trauma. This activation is facilitated through the stimulation of the vagus nerve, a critical component of the parasympathetic nervous system, which helps to lower heart rate, reduce blood pressure, and initiate a state of calm throughout the body. Additionally, shaking has been shown to disrupt the body's chronic stress patterns, effectively 'resetting' the nervous system to a more balanced state. This physiological shift not only alleviates symptoms of anxiety and tension but also paves the way for emotional release and healing.

Neurochemical Release: Engaging in shaking practices has been correlated with the release of neurochemicals such as dopamine and serotonin, which play key roles in mood regulation and a sense of well-being.

Muscle Relaxation: The rhythmic contraction and release inherent in shaking help to alleviate muscle tension, a common physical byproduct of emotional stress or trauma.

Guided Shaking Exercises

For those looking to incorporate shaking into their healing regimen, here are some step-by-step instructions for a simple yet effective shaking exercise:

1. Find a Comfortable Space: Choose a spot where you feel safe and won't be disturbed. Standing with

your feet shoulder-width apart, take a few deep breaths to center yourself.

2. Begin with Gentle Movement: Start by gently bouncing your knees, letting your arms hang loosely by your sides. Allow the movement to extend naturally through your body, from your legs to your torso, arms, and head.

3. Intensify the Shaking: Gradually let your movements become more vigorous. Shake your hands, wiggle your fingers, and let your whole body move freely. If comfortable, close your eyes to enhance your inward focus.

4. Use Breath as an Anchor: Maintain deep, rhythmic breathing throughout the exercise. This helps to support the release of tension and promotes a deeper sense of relaxation.

5. Wind Down Gradually: After several minutes, begin to slow your movements, transitioning from shaking to gentle swaying. Finally, come to a standstill, taking a moment to feel the sensations throughout your body.

This practice can be performed alone or in a group setting, with each offering its unique benefits. Group sessions, guided by a trained facilitator, can create a collective energy that enhances the experience of release and renewal.

Integrating Shaking with Other Therapies

Incorporating shaking and vibrational practices into a holistic healing approach can significantly enhance the process of recovery from trauma. Here are some ways shaking can complement other therapeutic modalities:

- Combination with Breathwork: Integrating shaking exercises with focused breathing techniques can amplify the relaxation response, deepening the sense of calm and facilitating a more profound release of trauma.
- Sequencing with Yoga or Dance: Starting a therapeutic session with shaking can serve to release initial layers of tension, making the body more receptive to the deeper stretches in yoga or the expressive movements in dance therapy.
- Incorporation into Psychotherapy: Shaking practices can be a valuable tool to physically release the emotions unearthed during counseling sessions, bridging the gap between cognitive understanding and somatic experience.

Creating a Safe Space for Movement

In the pursuit of emotional and physical healing through movement, the environment in which we practice holds significant influence over our experience. A space that radiates warmth, privacy, and tranquility can become a sanctuary for those seeking solace and strength through movement. This section is dedicated to crafting such an environment, whether in the solitude of your home or within the collective energy of a group setting.

Importance of a Nurturing Environment

The ambiance of a space can deeply affect our ability to connect with our bodies and emotions during movement practices. A nurturing environment acts as a supportive embrace, encouraging openness and vulnerability. It's in these settings that movement transcends mere physical activity, becoming a profound dialogue with our inner selves.

Elements of a Healing Space

Creating a personal space that supports healing through movement involves several key elements. Ensure your space offers privacy, a corner where the outside world's demands and judgments are momentarily kept at bay. This could mean using a room with a door you can close or setting up a screen in a part of a larger room. The physical comfort of your space is also vital. Ample room to move without restriction, a floor that supports your body, and the right temperature all contribute to a sense of well-being. Additionally, lighting plays a crucial role in setting the mood. Soft, gentle light can calm the mind, while brighter settings can energize. Consider using dimmable lights or candles. The inclusion of plants or elements of nature can also enhance the calming effect of your environment.

Make your space as unique as you are by infusing it with objects that hold meaning to you. These might be photographs, inspirational quotes, or anything that reminds you of peace, strength and healing.

Navigating Shared Spaces

For those without the luxury of a dedicated movement space, here are strategies to maintain a sense of safety and boundary:

- Timing: Choose times when the space is least likely to be needed by others, perhaps early morning or late evening.

- Portable Elements: Create a mobile kit of items that make a space feel personal and healing, such as a small rug, a cushion, or a scarf. These can be set up quickly and packed away after your practice.
- Communication: If you share your living space, communicate the importance of this practice to you and negotiate times or areas where you can have the privacy you need.

As WE WRAP up this exploration of setting up a nurturing environment for movement, the takeaway is clear: the space in which we engage in therapeutic movement deeply influences our healing process. Whether at home or in a group, the right environment can act as a cocoon, within which transformation and growth are nurtured.

SIX

CRAFTING YOUR SOMATIC SELF-CARE SANCTUARY

J ust as life brings forward continuous changes, your healing process is not static; it evolves, adapts, and grows with you. Your journey through somatic therapy and self-care requires attention, nurturing, and a routine that respects the seasons of your life. In this chapter, we will explore how creating a structured yet flexible routine can be your sanctuary, a space where healing flourishes.

The Importance of Routine in Healing

Creating a routine is like laying down a map for a road trip. It gives you a sense of direction, spots to visit, and where you might need to refuel. Similarly, a well-thought-out routine in healing provides structure, ensuring that the practices vital to your well-being are not left by the wayside in the hustle of daily life.

Building structure for healing

Imagine waking up each day knowing you have a set time for meditation, a moment carved out for journaling, or a specific hour for your body scan practice. This structure acts as a scaffold, supporting your healing process and ensuring that self-care becomes as natural as your morning cup of coffee.

Routine as a grounding tool

On days when life feels like a whirlwind, your routine can be the calm eye of the storm. For instance, no matter how chaotic a day gets, taking those ten minutes to breathe deeply or stretch can anchor you, providing a sense of normalcy and grounding.

The role of rituals

When somatic practices become rituals, they transcend mere activities, becoming sacred moments of connection with yourself. Lighting a candle before meditation or setting up a cozy corner for journaling can elevate these practices, imbuing them with deeper significance and enhancing their therapeutic effect.

Consistency and safety

For anyone healing from trauma, predictability can be soothing. A routine offers just that—a reliable framework within which you can explore, heal, and grow. It tells you, "Here, at this time, you are safe to focus on your well-being."

The following checklist is designed to guide you through creating a somatic healing routine tailored to your unique needs and lifestyle. By reflecting on your preferences, commitments, and rhythms, you can build a practice that nurtures your body, mind, and spirit.

1. **Choose Somatic Practices to Include**

   - Yoga
   - Meditation
   - Tai Chi or Qigong
   - Breathwork
   - Dancing
   - Nature Walks
   - Body Scans
   - Journaling
   - Other: _____

2. **Determine the Best Times for These Practices**

   Reflect on your daily and weekly schedule, your energy levels throughout the day, and how these practices can fit into your lifestyle seamlessly.

   - Early morning practices for energizing and setting intentions.
   - Midday sessions to refresh and refocus.
   - Evening routines for relaxation and unwinding.
   - Specific times that align with your natural rhythms

3. **Identify Simple Rituals to Elevate These Practices**

Rituals can transform your practices from routine to sacred, enhancing their impact.

- Lighting a candle or incense to signify the beginning of your practice.
- Creating a dedicated space filled with items that inspire tranquility.
- Playing soothing music or nature sounds.
- Using aromatherapy or essential oils.
- Starting with a short gratitude practice.
- Custom rituals: _____

4. Plan for Consistency While Allowing Flexibility

A flexible approach ensures your routine is sustainable and adaptable to life's inevitable changes.

- Set a goal for the frequency of your practice (daily, several times a week).
- Choose a primary practice but have 1-2 alternatives for variety or when time is limited.
- Remember the principle of gentleness: If you miss a session, simply resume the next day without self-criticism.
- Regularly assess and adjust your routine as needed.

5. Final Steps

- **Integrate**: Once you've completed this checklist, take some time to integrate your choices into a coherent routine. Sketch out a weekly schedule as a starting point.

- **Commit**: Commit to your routine for a set period (e.g., one month) before making any adjustments, allowing habits to form.
- **Reflect and Adjust**: At the end of your commitment period, reflect on what worked and what didn't. Adjust your routine accordingly, and set a new commitment period.

Remember, your personal checklist is not only a plan but a living document to your journey toward somatic healing. Regular reflection and adaptation will keep your practice aligned with your evolving needs and circumstances. This balance ensures that your healing practices are not just another task on your to-do list, but a cherished sanctuary. These moments of self-care are a precious reminder of your commitment to nurturing your well-being - of your commitment to yourself.

Building Your Somatic Self-Care Plan: A Step-by-Step Guide

When you first set out to create a personal somatic self-care plan, keep in mind that it should be a reflection of what *you* truly need in order to flourish. Here's a detailed guide to help you come up with a plan that supports your unique well-being and healing goals.

Assessing Individual Needs

The first step in this process involves a deep and honest look at what your needs actually are. It's about listening to your body and mind to understand where you're at and where you'd like to be. Start by asking yourself a series of questions:

When do I feel most at peace?

When do I feel most fulfilled and in alignment with my higher self?

What areas of my life (physical, emotional, mental) feel out of balance?

When do I feel most disconnected from myself?

What physical sensations or emotions arise regularly that I would like to address?

Reflecting on these questions helps pinpoint areas where somatic practices will bring you the most benefits. It's also useful to consider how external factors, such as work or relationships, impact your well-being. This holistic view forms the foundation of your self-care plan.

Selecting Somatic Techniques

With a clearer understanding of your needs, the next step is to explore somatic techniques that resonate with you. As we've already seen, there is a vast array of practices available, each offering unique benefits. When choosing techniques, think about what feels most appealing and manageable to you. It might be helpful to try a few different practices initially to see what best suits your needs.

Creating a Balanced Plan

A well-rounded self-care plan includes a variety of practices that address multiple aspects of well-being. To achieve this balance, it is vital to consider all three of the following:

- Physical: Incorporate activities that engage the body, like stretching or walking, to improve physical health and bodily awareness.
- Emotional: Choose practices that allow for emotional expression and processing, such as journaling or dance therapy.
- Mental: Include techniques focused on calming the mind, like meditation or breathwork, to reduce stress and enhance mental clarity.

Think about how these practices can fit into your daily and weekly routines. It might be helpful to designate certain activities for the morning to energize and prepare for the day, while others could be reserved for the evening to unwind and reflect.

Flexibility Within Structure

While having a structured plan is beneficial, it's equally important to remain flexible. Life is unpredictable, and your needs will inevitably change over time. Here are some tips for maintaining flexibility in your self-care routine.

1. Listen to Your Body and Mind: Regularly check in with yourself to assess how your chosen practices are serving you. If something doesn't feel right, be open to trying something new.
2. Adjust According to Life's Demands: If you find yourself going through a particularly busy or stressful period, it might be necessary to modify your plan to make it more manageable.

3. Be Open to Experimentation: As you evolve, so too will your self-care needs. Allow yourself the freedom to explore new techniques and practices that might better support your journey at any given time.

Tips for Staying Consistent with Your Practice

Establishing and maintaining a somatic healing routine is a process that can sometimes be challenging. The following are strategies designed to nurture your commitment, ensuring that these practices continue to support and grow with you throughout life.

Setting Realistic Goals

When we talk about goals, it's easy to aim high, often offering an ephemeral illusion of success. Yet, the key to creating a sustainable practice lies in setting targets that feel within your grasp. This approach encourages consistency whilst shielding you from the weight of discouragement that can creep in when goals seem too lofty.

Begin by identifying what you realistically can commit to each day or week. If ten minutes is all you have, let that be your starting point.

Break down larger aspirations into smaller, actionable steps. For instance, if your goal is to integrate body scanning into your routine, start with shorter sessions and gradually increase the duration as it becomes a more natural part of your day.

Remember, the aim is progress, not perfection. Allow your goals to adapt and evolve with your growing confidence and changing circumstances.

Incorporating Practices into Daily Life

Weaving somatic exercises into your everyday routine ensures they become as familiar and essential as your morning coffee or evening unwind time.

Identify activities where somatic practices can seamlessly fit. For example, performing a few mindful stretches during your morning shower or practicing deep breathing while waiting for your computer to boot up can turn idle moments into opportunities for self-care.

Use the transitions between different parts of your day as reminders. Shifting from work to home life, for example, can be an excellent time for a brief grounding exercise, helping to clear your mind and reset your energy.

Get creative with integration. Cooking dinner? Use the time to focus deeply on the sensations of the ingredients. Watching TV? Dedicate breaks to quick mindfulness or body awareness exercises.

Accountability Strategies

Staying on track with your somatic self-care routine can sometimes require a nudge. Employing strategies to keep yourself accountable ensures that your practice remains front and center.

1. Track Your Practices: Use a journal or an app to log your daily somatic activities. Visually seeing your progress can be a powerful motivator and a tool for reflection.
2. Set Reminders: Leverage technology by setting alarms or calendar reminders for your somatic

practices. These little prompts can be the gentle push needed to prioritize your self-care.

3. Partner with a Friend: Sharing your journey with a friend can significantly boost your accountability. Schedule check-ins to share experiences, challenges, and successes. This shared commitment can reinforce your motivation and provide support when it wanes.

Celebrating Progress

Recognizing and celebrating each step forward fuels your journey, turning even the smallest achievements into milestones. This practice of acknowledgment serves as a reminder of how far you've come and the growth you're cultivating each day.

- Take time to reflect on your progress, noting changes in your physical sensations, emotional state, and overall well-being since integrating somatic practices into your life.
- Celebrate the wins, no matter their size. Did you remember to take deep, mindful breaths during a stressful moment? Acknowledge it. Managed to keep up with your body scanning routine for a week? Reward yourself with something that enhances your practice, like a new journal or a comfortable meditation cushion.
- Share your victories with someone who understands and supports your journey. Sometimes, just voicing your progress can amplify its significance and motivate you to keep going.

Life seldom remains static. Changes, both subtle and significant, ripple through our existence, prompting us to reevaluate and adjust our sails. Amidst this flux, maintaining your healthy routines can feel like navigating uncharted waters. That's why I propose that we explore strategies for adapting your somatic practices to life's inevitable transitions, ensuring that your commitment to self-care remains steadfast.

Life Transitions

Transition periods are inevitable. Be they joyful or challenging, they often disrupt our established routines. Whether it's a new job, a move to a different city, or a change in relationship status, these shifts can upend the familiar, leaving us searching for solid ground. Therefore, adapting your somatic practices during these times will need to involve a few key steps.

1. Identify Core Practices: Pinpoint one or two somatic exercises that form the cornerstone of your routine. These should be practices that you can lean on, no matter the circumstances, offering a sense of continuity and stability.
2. Simplify: During times of transition, simplifying your routine can help maintain its essence without overwhelming you. If your usual practice spans an hour, consider how you can condense it into a 15-minute session that still captures its core benefits.
3. Portable Practices: Cultivate a set of exercises that don't rely on specific locations or equipment. Practices like mindful breathing, simple yoga poses,

or short meditations can be performed anywhere, ensuring you can maintain your routine, no matter where life takes you.

Flexibility for Busy Times

Even without major life changes, daily pressures can sometimes leave little room for extensive self-care routines. For these busy periods, having a repertoire of quick, adaptable somatic exercises ensures that self-care doesn't fall by the wayside. You can fall back on integrating micro-practices into your day. These are brief exercises, such as a two-minute deep breathing session or a series of gentle neck stretches, that can be done even during short breaks. Also, incorporating small doses of movement - movement snacks - throughout your day will allow you to keep looking after yourself when time is scarce. A series of squats while waiting for the kettle to boil or discreetly practicing foot grounding techniques under your desk can invigorate your body without needing dedicated time.

Emotional and Physical Shifts

Our bodies and minds are in a constant state of flux, influenced by internal and external factors. Emotional upheavals, hormonal changes, or physical injuries require us to listen closely to our bodies and adapt our practices accordingly.

Listening and Responding
Tune into your body's signals. If you're experiencing heightened emotional stress, prioritize practices that promote relaxation and grounding. Conversely, during periods of low energy or sadness, energizing movements might be more beneficial.

Modifying Practices

Adapt exercises to accommodate physical limitations. For instance, if you're recovering from an injury, modify yoga poses to avoid strain, or focus on seated meditation if movement is currently challenging. As a general guideline for somatics, make sure to pause often and listen to your body. Tuning in to your needs and respecting your limits is a vital component of this work.

Emotional Alignment

Align your practices with your emotional state. On days filled with anxiety, grounding techniques can provide calm. In contrast, on days where you feel disconnected or numb, engaging in more dynamic movements can awaken your senses and emotions.

Re-evaluating Needs

As I keep mentioning, the only constant in life is change. As we evolve, so do our somatic needs. Regularly taking stock of where you are in your healing process and how your needs have shifted is crucial for maintaining a routine that serves you.

Set aside time each week or month to reflect on your current somatic routine. Periodic check-ins allow you to reflect on what's working, what isn't, and why. This can help identify areas that need adjustment.

Be open to experimenting with new practices or revisiting ones you might have previously set aside. As your body and circumstances change, you might find different techniques resonate more strongly with you. If possible, seek feedback from a trusted therapist, coach, or fellow practitioners can provide new insights into how your routine might be refined to better support your growth. Our own perceptions can be limited and hinder our personal growth.

Tracking Progress and Making Adjustments

In the endeavor of nurturing oneself through somatic self-care, the act of journaling emerges as a pivotal ally. This practice acts as a mirror reflecting the nuances of your healing path, capturing shifts that might otherwise go unnoticed. By diligently jotting down thoughts, feelings, and bodily sensations associated with each somatic practice, you can create a tangible record of our journey.

Journaling as a Tool

Your journal is your trusted confidant, a safe space where every observation, no matter how small, is worthy of note. When you are ready, begin by recording the date, the somatic practices you engaged in, the duration, and any specific intentions set for each session. Afterward, reflect on and jot down the immediate physical sensations experienced during the practice, as well as any emotions or thoughts that surfaced. Over time, these entries compile into a comprehensive overview, unveiling the practices that resonate deeply with you and those that might require tweaking or replacement.

The feedback your body and mind offer is invaluable. As you pore over your journal entries, look for cues—perhaps a certain practice consistently evokes a sense of calm, or another leaves you feeling unsettled. Use these insights to fine-tune your somatic self-care plan. If a particular technique consistently aligns with feelings of peace and restoration, consider making it a more central part of your routine. Conversely, if another practice consistently stirs discomfort or dissonance, it might be time to explore alternatives that better suit your current state.

There are moments on this path where the guidance of a seasoned practitioner can be illuminating. If your journal reflections reveal persistent challenges or plateaus in your progress, reaching out for professional advice can offer new perspectives and strategies. A therapist or somatic coach can provide tailored suggestions based on your documented experiences, helping refine your practices to better align with your goals. They can also introduce you to new techniques that you might not have considered, enriching your self-care repertoire.

I hope this chapter has left you with the understanding that self-care is a dynamic, responsive practice. Throughout, we've uncovered the importance of attentive observation, the wisdom in our body's and mind's feedback, and the value of seeking external guidance when needed. We've explored the importance of patience, reminding ourselves that healing unfolds in its own time.

As WE TRANSITION from the introspective work of crafting and refining our self-care regimen, we will look ahead to the broader horizons of somatic therapy. In the next chapter, I invite you to extend your gaze outward, exploring how your individual healing journey resonates within the larger context of community and connection.

SEVEN

SOMATIC SOLUTIONS FOR ANXIETY

Anxiety is like having an alarm system in your body that's a bit too sensitive—it goes off even when there's no real danger. Imagine you're walking in a quiet street and suddenly a leaf rustles. Instead of just noticing and moving on, your body reacts as if a lion jumped out—it's trying to protect you, but it's overdoing it.

This alarm triggers a stress response, sometimes making your heart beat faster, your breathing quicken, and your muscles tighten. Preparing you to either run away or defend yourself, it's meant to help you in dangerous situations, but when you feel this way without a clear reason, it can be confusing and overwhelming. This state of high alert can make it hard to focus, relax, or enjoy things you normally would.

In short, anxiety is your body's way of responding to stress, but it's kicking in too often and too strongly, turning everyday situations into more stressful experiences than they need to be. Needless to say, this takes a huge toll on your overall health and well-being.

As we dive into this section, let's attempt to understand

anxiety not just as a psychological phenomenon, but as a deeply embodied experience that impacts us at our very core. Throughout this exploration, we'll look at anxiety through the innovative realm of somatic healing. We'll look at the intricate ways in which our bodies communicate emotional distress, which will allow us to recognize, acknowledge, and transform anxiety through practices rooted in bodily awareness. The aim is to integrate our body's sensations, movements, and intuitive wisdom to uncover triggers and begin healing the physical and psychological damage that results from this common form of ongoing stress.

Let's learn to engage with anxiety in a compassionate, embodied way, healing shadows on the way and renewing a deep sense of emotional liberation.

Exercises for Anxiety

Quite honestly, I used to catch myself regularly constricting my breath in moments of busyness or stress. Breathing is our most fundamental connection to life, yet in times of anxiety, our breath often becomes shallow, rapid, and constricted. By consciously changing our breathing patterns, we can signal the brain to activate the body's natural relaxation response.

Diaphragmatic Breathing

This involves deep breathing through the diaphragm rather than shallow breathing from the chest. To practice, place one hand on your chest and the other on your belly. Breathe in deeply through your nose, ensuring that the hand on your belly rises higher than the one on your chest. Exhale slowly through pursed lips.

4-7-8 Breathing Technique

Yes, this again! I need to emphasize just how powerful this technique is, especially once fully integrated as an automatic calming mechanism. If you haven't included this in your regular practice yet, it's time to give it a try.

Breathe in through your nose for a count of four, hold your breath for seven counts, and then exhale completely through your mouth for a count of eight. Repeat at least three consecutive times. This method helps reduce anxiety by increasing the amount of oxygen in your bloodstream and promoting a state of balance within the nervous system.

Add to breathwork other practices we've already explored, such as grounding techniques and mindful movement. These will be highly effective and help redirect your focus from the anxiety-inducing thoughts to the present moment, anchoring you in the here and now. They will also allow for the expression and release of pent-up energy and emotions that result from your body's physiological stress response.

Establishing a Safe Space

Creating a physical and mental space where you feel secure and at ease is crucial for managing anxiety. This space serves as a sanctuary where the practices of somatic therapy can unfold.

Your physical environment is often a reflection of your inner world and, in turn, influences the state of your mental well-being. Choose or create a quiet, comfortable spot where you won't be disturbed. Personalize it with items that evoke a sense of calm, such as soft blankets, soothing scents, or calming colors.

As you step into your safe space, take a moment to mentally

affirm your commitment to nurturing your well-being. Choose a statement of gratitude to remind yourself of how fortunate you are to have access to this calm and safe place. Acknowledge that this time is a gift to yourself, a step towards reclaiming your inner peace.

It's important to see anxiety not as an invader to be battled, but as a signal to be understood and harmonized with. These practices—breathing exercises, grounding techniques, mindful movement, and the creation of a safe space—invite us to tune back into our body's natural rhythms, transforming the discord of anxiety into a symphony of calmness.

Addressing Depression Through Somatic Methods

In a world that can often feel drenched in shadow, somatic practices emerge as pathways out of the darkness of depression. The essence of these methods lie not in escaping our feelings but in meeting them with awareness, movement, and connection. It's through these channels we find routes to lift the fog of disconnection and numbness, making space for vibrancy and vitality to flow back into our lives.

Body Awareness and Depression

Depression can create a chasm between mind and body, enveloping us in a numbness that detaches us from the richness of living. Cultivating body awareness acts as a bridge across this divide, gently reintroducing us to the sensations, emotions, and experiences we've been missing. Techniques like mindful meditation focus attention on bodily sensations, teaching us to observe without judgment. This heightened awareness can slowly peel away layers of numbness, allowing us to reconnect with the subtle yet profound joys of sensory experience—like the warmth of sunlight on skin or the comforting weight of a blanket.

Energizing Movement Practices

Movement possesses a dual power to ground us in the present and elevate our spirits. For those weighed down by depression, energizing movement practices can act as a gentle but effective catalyst for emotional uplift. Consider incorporating:

- Dynamic Yoga Flows: Unlike more meditative forms, dynamic yoga introduces a series of flowing postures that build heat and energy within the body, sparking a lightness in spirit.
- Aerobic Exercise: Activities like brisk walking, jogging, or cycling increase heart rate and circulation, promoting the release of endorphins—nature's mood lifters.
- Dance: Freeform dance, in particular, invites spontaneity and joy. It encourages an exploration of movement that doesn't just move the body but also moves emotions, allowing for an expressive release.

These practices don't necessitate intensity or long durations; even short, regular sessions can significantly impact mood and energy levels.

Nature Therapy

Depression often isolates us, not just from others but from the world itself. Integrating nature into somatic practices is a powerful antidote to this isolation, rekindling our bond with the environment and, by extension, with life. Nature therapy involves activities such as:

- Forest Bathing: Simply being in the presence of trees and greenery can lower stress hormone levels, improve mood, and enhance cognitive function.
- Gardening: Engaging in gardening connects us to the cycles of growth and renewal, mirroring our healing process.
- Outdoor Yoga or Tai Chi: Practicing these disciplines outdoors combines the benefits of movement with the restorative effects of being in nature, offering a double dose of healing.

My personal go-to nature therapy activity is a daily sunrise beach walk and ocean swim - however, keep in mind that there are many different and unique ways in which to engage in this. The key here is simply the sensory immersion in nature—feeling the breeze, hearing birdsong, and seeing the myriad shades of green that signal growth and life.

Rituals for Reconnection

Creating rituals around somatic practices can deepen their impact, turning them into sacred acts of reconnection with oneself, others, and the world. These rituals can take many forms, such as:

- Morning Rituals: Start the day with a simple routine that incorporates a somatic practice, setting a positive and connected tone for the day ahead.

- Gratitude Practices: End each day by reflecting on moments of connection or joy, however small. This can reframe perspectives, highlighting the threads of positivity that weave through even the toughest days.
- Community Connection: Engage in group somatic practices, whether it's a yoga class, dance group, or hiking club. The shared experience can diminish feelings of isolation, reminding us of our place within a larger community.

These methods are points of stability within the chaos of life. They provide focus in the turbulence of depression, guiding us back to a sense of connection and belonging.

In exploring these somatic methods—body awareness, energizing movement, nature therapy, and rituals of reconnection—we find strategies for coping with depression that become pathways to a richer, more connected way of living. Each step taken, each breath drawn, and each moment spent in nature or movement creates a stronger, more vibrant thread into the fabric of our lives. This gradually dispels the darkness of depression with the light of awareness, movement, and connection.

Physical trauma, whether from an injury, accident, or surgery, leaves imprints not just on the body but also on the emotional landscape of an individual. The aftermath often carries a dual burden: the physical pain and limitations, coupled with emotional responses such as fear, frustration, and a sense of vulnerability. Recognizing the intertwined nature of these responses opens up pathways for healing that go beyond conventional medical treatments, truly delving into the realm of somatic therapy.

Somatic therapy, with its holistic focus on the relationship between body and mind, provides tools and techniques that can be particularly beneficial for those recovering from physical trauma. It acknowledges the body's remarkable capacity for healing and aims to support this process by addressing both the physical and emotional aspects of recovery.

Somatic Experiencing for Physical Trauma

One of the key techniques in somatic therapy tailored to physical trauma recovery is Somatic Experiencing (SE). Developed by Dr. Peter Levine, SE is based on the observation that animals in the wild do not suffer from trauma despite regularly facing life-threatening situations. They manage to "shake off" the energy from such experiences, something humans have lost touch with due to our complex brains and societal norms.

SE introduces this concept to trauma recovery, guiding us through exercises that help release the 'stuck' energy and stress responses trapped in our bodies since the trauma. For someone recovering from a physical injury, this might involve:

- Tracking Sensations: Gently becoming aware of bodily sensations, differentiating between those associated with trauma and those signaling recovery.
- Titration and Pendulation: Gradually revisiting the traumatic experience in small doses (titration) and oscillating between the trauma and resources that offer relief (pendulation), facilitating a controlled release of pent-up stress.
- Discharge: Engaging in exercises that allow the body to physically release trapped energy, which might manifest as trembling, heat, or spontaneous movement.

Rebuilding Trust in the Body

Physical trauma can severely disrupt one's relationship with their body, leading to distrust and disconnection. Rebuilding this trust is a critical step in the healing process. Some strategies include mindful movement, visualization, and therapeutic touch. Engaging in gentle, mindful exercises can help reestablish a sense of control and agency over one's body. Focusing on movements that feel safe and restorative encourages a positive reconnection with the body. Imagining the body healing, envisioning wounds knitting together and strength returning, can foster a supportive mental environment that complements physical recovery. As for therapeutic touch, whether through professional massage or self-administered techniques like gentle rubbing or patting areas of tension, reinforces the body's capacity for pleasure and relaxation, countering the memories of pain.

Integrative Practices

For those on the path to recovery from physical trauma, integrating somatic therapy with conventional medical treatment offers a holistic approach to healing.

This integration might look like:

- Physical Therapy with a Somatic Lens: Working with physical therapists who are open to incorporating somatic elements into rehabilitation exercises can enhance the healing process. This could involve focusing on bodily sensations during physical therapy sessions or incorporating breathing exercises to manage pain.
- Collaborative Care Teams: Assembling a care team that includes medical professionals, somatic therapists, and mental health practitioners ensures that all aspects of recovery are addressed. Open communication and collaboration among team members facilitate a unified approach to healing.
- Personalized Healing Plans: Recognizing the uniqueness of each person's experience with trauma, integrative practices emphasize creating personalized healing plans. This might involve adjusting the balance between different therapies based on progress and evolving needs.

Through somatic experiencing, mindful movement, and the integration of conventional and holistic therapies, a path toward wholeness and well-being is not just imagined but actively forged.

Within us, emotions flow like rivers, sometimes meandering gently, at other times rushing fiercely. Yet, when obstacles interrupt this flow, our emotional currents can stagnate, leading to blockages that impact our physical and mental well-being. Understanding how to recognize, release, and maintain the fluidity of these emotional currents is crucial for holistic health. This section guides you through navigating the landscape of emotional blockages with the aid of somatic therapy.

Identifying Emotional Blockages

Our bodies can serve as maps to our inner emotional states, with certain areas acting as repositories for unexpressed emotions. Recognizing these blockages requires attunement to the subtle cues our bodies provide. At times, these blockages can look and feel like:

- Tension: Persistent tension in areas like the shoulders, neck, or jaw can indicate harbored stress or unexpressed anger.
- Discomfort: Recurring discomfort or pain in specific body parts, without a clear physical cause, might signal underlying emotional distress.
- Breathing Patterns: Shallow, restricted breathing can be a response to anxiety or fear, suggesting an emotional blockage that limits full respiratory expansion.

Tuning into these bodily sensations with curiosity rather than judgment allows for the first step in acknowledging and addressing emotional blockages.

Releasing Techniques

Once blockages are identified, somatic therapy offers a variety of techniques to facilitate their release, encouraging the resumption of emotional flow. Some effective methods include:

- Expressive Movement: This practice invites spontaneous, uninhibited movement, allowing the body to move as it wishes without choreography or structure. It can unlock and express emotions that have been stifled or unacknowledged, serving as a powerful outlet for release.
- Breathwork: Specific breathing techniques, such as deep diaphragmatic breathing or rhythmic breath cycles, can directly impact our emotional state. By consciously altering our breathing patterns, we can release emotional tension and foster a sense of calm.
- Vocalization: Using the voice through humming, chanting, or singing can help release blockages related to communication and self-expression. The vibration of vocalization can be particularly effective in loosening the tightness in the throat and chest areas.

Incorporating these practices into a regular self-care routine will promote release and recovery, whilst paving the way for the continuous flow of emotions, preventing the formation of new blockages.

Fostering Emotional Fluidity

To maintain an open and fluid emotional state, it's essential to cultivate practices that encourage regular emotional expression and processing. Consider the following:

- Daily Check-ins: Dedicate a few moments each day to check in with your body and emotions. This can be a quiet time of reflection or a brief journaling session where you note any areas of tension and the emotions they might be harboring.
- Creative Expression: Engage in creative activities such as painting, writing, or playing music. These outlets offer alternative ways to process and express emotions, contributing to emotional fluidity.
- Mindfulness Meditation: Regular mindfulness practice can heighten body awareness and sensitivity to emotional states, allowing for earlier recognition of emotional blockages and facilitating their release.

These practices assist in releasing current blockages, also playing a preventive role by ensuring emotions continue to flow freely and healthily.

Support Systems and Resources

While self-help practices are invaluable, navigating deep-seated emotional blockages often requires the guidance of professionals. Here are some avenues to consider:

- Somatic Therapy Professionals: Seek out therapists who specialize in somatic practices. Their expertise in the connection between body and emotion can provide tailored guidance for identifying and releasing blockages.

- Workshops and Groups: Participating in workshops or group sessions focused on somatic practices can offer both professional guidance and the support of a community with similar experiences.
- Online Resources: Numerous online platforms offer resources ranging from instructional videos on somatic techniques to forums for sharing experiences and advice. These can be valuable supplements to personal and professional support.

Navigating emotional blockages through somatic therapy is a delicate balance of recognizing when to move and when to pause, when to push forward and when to yield. This dance is not always straightforward, but it is deeply rewarding. Through the practices of identifying blockages, releasing them, fostering emotional fluidity, and leaning on support systems, we equip ourselves with the tools to ensure our emotions flow unimpeded, enriching every aspect of our lives with their vitality and depth.

Enhancing Self-Esteem and Body Image

In a world that often bombards us with unrealistic standards of beauty and success, it's no surprise that many struggle with self-esteem and body image. However, turning inward and connecting with our bodies through somatic practices can open doors to greater self-acceptance and appreciation. These methods help us to recognize our worth, as well as to celebrate the unique journey of our bodies through life.

Body Neutrality and Acceptance

Moving towards a stance of body neutrality and acceptance is the first step in reshaping how we view ourselves. This approach encourages us to view our bodies through a lens of functionality and gratitude, rather than solely appearance. Practices such as mindful meditation focused on gratitude for the body's capabilities can be transformative. For instance, dedicating moments to thank our legs for carrying us through the day or our hands for their ability to create and connect can shift the narrative from criticism to appreciation.

Another effective practice involves body mapping, where one creates a visual representation of their body, marking areas of strength, resilience, and even pain with symbols or colors. This exercise not only fosters an intimate understanding of one's physical self but also highlights the body's journey and inherent worth beyond aesthetic standards.

Empowerment Through Movement

Movement practices offer a dynamic pathway to feeling empowered in our own skin. Engaging in activities that emphasize the body's strength, flexibility, and presence can dramatically improve self-esteem. For example, martial arts or strength training can be particularly empowering, as they focus on what the body can achieve and endure, rather than how it looks.

Similarly, dance provides a powerful medium to explore and express our identity freely. It teaches us to take up space confidently and to value our bodies for their expressive potential rather than their conformity to societal norms.

Mirror Work and Self-Compassion

Mirror work involves standing in front of a mirror and engaging in positive self-talk, affirmations, or even simply observing oneself with kindness and compassion. While this practice may initially feel uncomfortable for some, it gradually helps in breaking down the barriers of self-criticism and fosters a more compassionate relationship with oneself.

Coupled with self-compassion exercises—such as writing letters to yourself with words of understanding, acceptance, and love—mirror work can significantly impact how we perceive and value ourselves.

Celebrating the Body

Recognizing and celebrating the body's capabilities and uniqueness can significantly shift the focus from appearance to appreciation. Practices that encourage this shift include:

- Creating a Joy List: Compile activities that make your body feel good, like stretching, walking in nature, or swimming. Regularly engaging in these activities reinforces the body's role in providing joy and satisfaction.
- Body Positive Yoga: Participate in yoga classes that emphasize body positivity, focusing on how poses feel rather than how they look, and adapting practices to suit all body types and abilities.
- Sharing Stories: Participate in groups or forums where people share their journeys of body acceptance and self-love. Hearing others' experiences can be affirming and inspiring, reminding us that we are not alone in our struggles with self-esteem and body image.

In cultivating practices that nourish a healthy relationship with our bodies, we embark on a path of healing and self-discovery. Embracing body neutrality, finding empowerment in movement, practicing self-compassion, and celebrating our bodies lays the foundation for lasting self-esteem and a positive body image.

As WE CONCLUDE this exploration of enhancing self-esteem and body image through somatic practices, we're reminded of the transformative power of connecting with our bodies. These practices lead to an unconditional acceptance and appreciation of our physical selves whilst contributing to a broader sense of well-being and fulfillment. They remind us that our bodies are not adversaries to be critiqued but companions on our life's journey, deserving of care, respect, and celebration.

EIGHT
DEEP DIVES AND NEW HORIZONS

Picture yourself standing, nervously swaying at the edge of a diving board for the first time.

Below you, the water promises refreshing new insights but also hints at the challenge of the plunge.

This moment, right here, encapsulates the essence of exploring Somatic Experiencing beyond the basics. This work is about taking that leap, armed with trust in the resilience of your own body and spirit, to uncover deeper layers of healing.

Now, let's move from the edge and take that dive into the depths of advanced somatic practices, where the true transformation unfolds.

Foundations of Somatic Experiencing

Somatic Experiencing stands as a safe and supportive pathway for those navigating trauma. Rooted in the observation that animals in the wild naturally discharge stress without lingering effects, this therapy offers guidelines for humans to release and resolve the physical manifestations of trauma.

At its core, SE shifts the focus from recounting traumatic events to tuning into the body's subtle cues, leading to a profound release and rebalancing of the nervous system.

Consider a moment when your heart raced at the memory of a stressful event. SE teaches techniques to ground yourself in such moments, using the body's wisdom to transform panic into peace.

Advanced Exercises

Beyond the foundational practices, SE offers a variety of advanced exercises tailored for deep trauma work. These exercises invite a nuanced exploration of bodily sensations, encouraging the nervous system to reset its response to past traumas.

TERMS TO FAMILIARIZE YOURSELF WITH:

- Resourcing: Identifying and tapping into internal and external resources that provide a sense of safety and stability.
- Pendulation: Gently oscillating between sensations associated with trauma and those linked to resources, facilitating a natural rhythm of activation and settling in the nervous system.
- Coupling Dynamics: Observing how contrasting sensations interact within the body, such as warmth and coolness or tension and relaxation, to foster integration and healing.

The power of SE is utterly transformative. One compelling case (similar to so many others) involved a firefighter struggling with PTSD after a particularly harrowing rescue operation.

Through progressive SE, he was able to reconnect with his body's innate resilience, gradually finding peace in moments that once triggered intense flashbacks.

Remember, SE has the capacity to mend the fractures trauma leaves in its wake, guiding us back to a sense of wholeness and balance.

The SE Process

To help you familiarize yourself with the Somatic Experiencing process, I have created a representation of the sequence and key elements of the therapy, from the initial steps to final stages.

Here's your structured breakdown of how the SE process can be depicted:

1. Introduction to SE and Building Resources

OBJECTIVE: Prepare ourselves by building a sense of safety and resilience.

KEY CONCEPTS:

- Grounding techniques
- Establishing a safe environment
- Identifying internal resources

2. Titration and Pendulation

.   .   .

OBJECTIVE: Gently approach traumatic memories without becoming overwhelmed.

KEY CONCEPTS:

- Titration: Introducing small amounts of traumatic material
- Pendulation: Moving back and forth between regulation and dysregulation

3. Identifying and Releasing Trauma

OBJECTIVE: Identify, process, and release trauma stored in the body.

KEY CONCEPTS:

- Tracking bodily sensations
- Releasing stored trauma through physical responses

4. Integration

.   .   .

OBJECTIVE: Integrate the processed experiences into a coherent sense of self.

KEY CONCEPTS:

- Reflecting on changes in perception and self-awareness
- Stabilizing the new state of balance

5. Expansion and Growth

OBJECTIVE: Practice ongoing self-awareness and resilience after therapy.

KEY CONCEPTS:

- Developing new coping strategies
- Encouraging emotional and physiological resilience

Reflection Questions

In the journey of healing and self-discovery through Somatic Experiencing, reflection plays a crucial role. This section of the book provides a series of questions designed to deepen your understanding of SE principles and enhance your application of its techniques. As you explore these questions, consider adding to your journal to document your thoughts and experiences. This practice can be instrumental in facilitating personal growth and healing.

Once completed, remember that these reflection questions are meant to be revisited periodically throughout your therapy journey. Each time you return to them, you might discover new insights or observe changes in your responses. I promise you that engaging deeply and regularly with these questions will enhance your understanding of somatic healing principles and improve your therapeutic outcomes.

---

1. Reflecting on Body Sensations and Stress

What sensations do I notice in my body when recalling a stressful event, and how can I ground myself in the present?

Identify specific physical sensations (tightness, heat, shivering, etc.) associated with stress. Reflect on various grounding techniques, such as deep breathing, feeling your feet on the ground, or focusing on sensory experiences (sight, sound, touch), and consider which methods most effectively bring you back to the present moment.

2. Accessing Internal Resources

How do my internal resources feel in my body, and how can I access these sensations in moments of distress?

Focus on recognizing feelings of strength, calm, or resilience within your body. These might manifest as a warm feeling in your chest or a sense of solidity in your feet. Consider how you can intentionally connect with these sensations during challenging times to cultivate a sense of stability and safety.

_____

_____

_____

_____

_____

_____

_____

_____

_____

_____

_____

_____

3. Understanding Pendulation

In what ways have I observed pendulation in my own healing process, and how can I consciously engage with this rhythm?

Reflect on moments when you've naturally oscillated between feeling emotionally or physically overwhelmed and a state of relaxation or neutrality. Identify triggers and calming factors, and think about how you can actively use this understanding to help manage your reactions in a healing context.

_____

_____

_____

_____

_____

_____

_____

_____

_____

_____

_____

The Role of Polyvagal Theory in Somatic Therapy

In the fascinating realm of somatic therapy, the polyvagal theory stands out as a pivotal framework that reshapes our understanding of the body's response to stress and trauma. This theory, introduced by Dr. Stephen Porges, reveals the intricate ways in which our nervous system mediates our interactions with the world, influencing our capacity for safety, connection, and healing. At its heart, polyvagal theory elucidates how different states of our autonomic nervous system dictate our experiences of safety and danger, fundamentally altering our approach to therapy and self-regulation.

Understanding polyvagal theory begins with recognizing the three primary states of the autonomic nervous system: the ventral vagal state, associated with feelings of safety and social connection; the sympathetic state, linked to the fight or flight response; and the dorsal vagal state, related to shutdown and disconnection. Grasping this triad is crucial for interpreting our bodily sensations and emotional responses as signals of these underlying physiological states, rather than isolated experiences.

With this understanding, somatic therapy integrates polyvagal principles to foster a sense of safety and connection, foundational elements for healing. The aim is for us to identify which state we are operating from and employ techniques designed to shift towards a more regulated, ventral vagal state. This process involves cultivating an environment of safety, both internally and externally, where the nervous system can relax and open up to connection and healing.

Specific exercises based on polyvagal theory are instrumental in this shift. These practices might include:

- Deep, slow breathing: This can signal the body to shift from a sympathetic state to a ventral vagal state, promoting calm and a sense of safety.
- Social engagement: Simple acts of connection, like making eye contact or engaging in gentle conversation, can activate the ventral vagal system, reinforcing feelings of safety and trust.
- Muscle relaxation techniques: Consciously relaxing the muscles, especially around the neck and face, can encourage a shift away from fight or flight responses, inviting a sense of calm and groundedness.
- Grounding exercises: Practices that enhance bodily awareness and present-moment experience can help pull individuals out of the dorsal vagal state of shutdown, reconnecting them with their surroundings and themselves.

Incorporating an awareness of polyvagal states into daily life transforms how we navigate our world and interact with others. Simple yet profound shifts in our routines can reinforce a ventral vagal state, enhancing our sense of connection and well-being. Here are a few simple tips for integrating this awareness.

1. Routine mindfulness: Taking moments throughout the day to check in with ourselves, noting our current state and using grounding or breathing exercises as needed.
2. Cultivating connection: Prioritizing genuine social interactions that foster a sense of belonging and safety, from sharing a meal with loved ones to engaging in community activities.

3. Physical touch: Engaging in safe, consensual physical touch, such as hugs or hand-holding, which can significantly bolster the ventral vagal system and reinforce feelings of connection and security.

4. Laughter and play: Activities that evoke joy and laughter naturally stimulate the ventral vagal system, promoting relaxation and a sense of communal bonding.

By including the principles of polyvagal theory into somatic healing practices and our daily lives, we unlock new avenues for understanding and influencing our body's response to the world. This approach does not merely address symptoms but targets the underlying physiological states that shape our experiences of safety, connection, and ultimately, healing. Through informed practices and mindful incorporation of polyvagal insights, we can navigate our healing process with a deeper sense of agency and compassion for our body's innate wisdom and resilience.

Titration: A Technique for Managing Intense Emotions

In the realm of somatic therapy, titration is a method that stands out for its gentle approach to processing and releasing intense emotions. This technique, akin to adding a drop of dye to water and watching it slowly disperse, involves experiencing emotions in small, manageable doses. This careful, measured approach ensures that we are not overwhelmed by our feelings, making the process of emotional healing more accessible and less daunting.

Titration in somatic therapy is inspired by the chemical process of the same name, where substances are combined in a controlled manner to prevent adverse reactions. Similarly, this technique acknowledges the potency of our emotions and the impact they can have on our psychological and physiological state. By breaking down the experience of intense emotions into smaller, digestible pieces, titration allows individuals to engage with their feelings without the risk of re-traumatization or overwhelm.

The practice of titration is particularly effective for those who have faced trauma. For these individuals, emotions linked to past events can often feel too intense or frightening to confront all at once. Titration offers a pathway to healing that respects the body's and the mind's limits, encouraging a slow and steady engagement with difficult emotions.

Guided Titration Exercises

Implementing titration into somatic therapy involves a series of guided exercises that facilitate a gradual emotional release. The following are simplified steps to illustrate the process.

1. Finding a Safe Starting Point: Begin by identifying a neutral or positive memory, sensation, or thought to serve as a grounding point. This will be your safe harbor to return to if the emotional waters get too rough.
2. Introducing the Emotional Stimulus: Gently bring to mind a challenging emotion or memory, but only to the extent that you can handle without feeling overwhelmed. This might mean only thinking about the event in the broadest terms or focusing on a single aspect of it.

3. Monitoring the Response: Pay close attention to how your body reacts to this stimulus. Notice any changes in breathing, muscle tension, or heart rate, and observe any emotions that surface.
4. Returning to Safety: Before the emotional response becomes too intense, shift your focus back to your safe point, allowing your body and mind to calm.
5. Repeating the Process: Gradually, and over time, you can return to the emotional stimulus, each time venturing a little further into the emotion as your capacity to process it increases.

Benefits of Titration

The titration method offers several benefits that make it a valuable tool in the healing process:

- Prevents Overwhelm: By breaking down the experience of intense emotions into manageable pieces, titration ensures that individuals do not become overwhelmed, making the therapy process safer and more approachable.
- Cultivates Emotional Resilience: Each successful engagement with challenging emotions strengthens the individual's confidence and ability to cope, building resilience over time.
- Encourages Deep Healing: Titration allows for a thorough and deep processing of emotions, as it enables individuals to engage with the full spectrum of their feelings at a pace that they can handle.
- Supports Self-regulation: Through the practice of shifting focus between emotional stimuli and

safety, individuals learn valuable self-regulation skills that are beneficial beyond the therapy session.

Incorporating Titration into Practice

Incorporating titration into one's somatic practice, whether independently or with a therapist, involves a few key considerations:

- With a Therapist: Working with a therapist skilled in somatic techniques can provide the necessary guidance and support to navigate titration effectively. A therapist can help identify appropriate starting points, monitor the process, and provide immediate support if the emotional intensity becomes too great.
- Independently: For those practicing titration on their own, it's crucial to have a clear understanding of the technique and to approach the process with patience and self-compassion. Keeping a journal to document the experience can offer insights into patterns and progress.
- Creating a Supportive Environment: Whether practicing titration solo or with professional guidance, ensuring that the environment is conducive to relaxation and safety is vital. This might include a quiet space, comfortable seating, and the absence of distractions.
- Combining with Other Techniques: Titration can be effectively combined with other somatic practices, such as grounding exercises or mindful breathing, to enhance the process of emotional release and regulation.

By thoughtfully integrating titration into somatic therapy, we are offered a compassionate pathway to confront and heal from intense emotions. This technique respects the natural capacity for emotional processing, providing a structured yet flexible approach to navigate the complex terrain of healing. Through titration, the daunting task of facing our deepest fears and pains becomes a journey marked by gradual discovery, resilience, and profound transformation.

Integrating Somatic Therapy with Other Healing Modalities

Uniting somatic therapy with other healing approaches creates a network of wellness strategies that address the multifaceted nature of individual healing needs. This synergy allows for a more rounded approach, addressing not just the symptoms but the root causes of emotional and physical discomfort. Here, we delve into how blending somatic therapy with psychotherapy, art therapy, mindfulness practices, and shadow work can offer a holistic path to well-being.

Blending Somatic Therapy and Psychotherapy

While somatic therapy focuses on bodily sensations and the non-verbal cues related to trauma and stress, psychotherapy often centers on verbal expression, exploring thoughts, beliefs, and personal history. When these two modalities converge, they offer a dual pathway to healing. Somatic therapy can unlock and release trapped emotional energy in the body, which might be too difficult to access through words alone. Psychotherapy provides a space to process these releases cognitively, allowing for insight and understanding, which can be critical for long-term emotional health.

This integrated approach can be particularly effective for

individuals who feel stuck in their healing process, as it engages both the mind and body in the journey towards recovery.

Art Therapy and Somatic Practices: A Creative Union

Art therapy, with its emphasis on expression through creativity, naturally complements somatic therapy's focus on bodily awareness. This combination allows individuals to explore their internal landscape not just through physical sensations but through visual and tactile forms.

Drawing, painting, or sculpting physical sensations or emotions that arise during somatic exercises can provide a tangible form to abstract experiences, making them easier to understand and process. Moreover, engaging in art immediately after somatic practices can capture the raw, unfiltered essence of the emotional and physical release, providing deep insights into personal healing symbols and themes.

For many, this creative process becomes a powerful tool for non-verbal communication, offering a different lens through which to view and understand their healing journey.

The Symbiosis of Mindfulness Practices and Somatic Healing

Mindfulness practices, with their emphasis on present-moment awareness, naturally enhance the benefits of somatic therapy. By fostering an acute awareness of bodily sensations and thoughts, mindfulness practices can amplify the effectiveness of somatic work. For instance, mindfulness meditation before somatic exercises can deepen the state of bodily awareness, making it easier to connect with and release trapped emotions. Mindful walking or yoga can be seen as somatic exercises in themselves, promoting a harmonious blend of physical movement and conscious awareness.

For individuals seeking to deepen their connection with their bodies and emotions, incorporating mindfulness into their somatic therapy regimen offers a path that enriches both practices.

Shadow work, a concept in psychology introduced by Carl Jung, involves exploring the darker, unconscious parts of our personality that we often deny or suppress. When paired with somatic healing, these two practices can offer profound mental, emotional, and physical benefits. Here's how integrating shadow work with somatic healing can be utterly transformative.

Mental Benefits

Shadow work encourages self-awareness and insight, helping us recognize and understand hidden emotions and motivations that influence our behavior. By incorporating somatic practices, we can physically experience where these suppressed emotions manifest in the body, such as tension or discomfort in specific areas. This awareness can lead to a clearer and more cohesive mental state, reducing anxiety and creating a greater sense of peace and mental clarity.

Emotional Benefits

Engaging in shadow work helps bring repressed feelings to the surface. It can be an intense process, as facing one's inner darkness is not easy. Somatic healing supports this by helping the body process and release these emotions. Techniques like deep breathing, mindfulness, and physical movement allow us to experience our emotions in real-time and let them go more effectively. This process can lead to improved emotional resilience and healthier coping mechanisms.

Physical Benefits

Somatic practices emphasize the connection between emotional health and physical health, and working through our psychological shadows often leads to experiencing physical relief related to decreased emotional burden. Chronic pains, aches, and tensions that are manifestations of emotional distress can be alleviated as the body releases the underlying emotional blockages.

———

Here are some practical tips to combine shadow work and somatic healing:

Start with Awareness: Begin by becoming aware of your physical sensations and emotional states. Regularly check in with your body through the various somatic practices we have discussed, and learn to understand where you might be holding emotional tension.

- **Journaling and Reflection:** Use journaling to explore thoughts and feelings that arise during or after somatic exercises. This can help link physical sensations with emotional experiences, a key aspect of shadow work.
- **Guided Imagery:** Employ guided imagery during somatic exercises to confront and communicate with shadow aspects. For example, while in a relaxed state induced by deep breathing, visualize meeting a part of yourself that you dislike or fear and engage in a mental dialogue with this aspect. This will also be highly beneficial to support inner child work.
- **Integrate Regular Practice:** Make both practices a regular part of your routine.

Consistency is key in achieving deep and lasting transformation. Allow your experiences in shadow work to inform your somatic practices and vice versa.

Incorporating somatic therapy into a broader spectrum of healing modalities offers a holistic approach that honors the complexity of the human experience. By acknowledging and nurturing the interconnectedness of mind, body, and spirit, we can explore a more comprehensive path to personal growth.

The Future of Somatic Therapy: Trends and Innovations

In recent times, the field of somatic therapy has begun to glitter with new research findings and innovative practices, signaling a promising horizon for this healing modality. The landscape is evolving, shaped by advancements that bring fresh perspectives and expand the toolkit available to practitioners like yourself. This section explores the dynamic shifts and possibilities that are charting the future of somatic therapies.

Emerging Research

A wave of recent studies has started to solidify the scientific foundation of somatic therapy, offering compelling evidence of its efficacy. Researchers are exploring the intricate ways bodily sensations and movements influence psychological well-being, with findings that underscore the therapy's potential in treating a wide range of conditions, from PTSD to chronic pain. Notably, neuroscientific investigations into the body-mind connection are revealing how somatic practices can rewire neural pathways, offering a biological explanation for the profound changes practitioners experience. This burgeoning body of research validates the experiences of those who have found healing through somatic therapy and paves the way for its broader acceptance in the therapeutic community.

Innovative Practices

The horizon of somatic therapy is expanding with the introduction of innovative practices that blend traditional techniques with cutting-edge technologies. Virtual reality (VR), for instance, is being explored as a tool to create immersive environments that facilitate somatic exploration and healing. By simulating scenarios that evoke bodily responses, VR offers a unique platform for clients to safely engage with and process traumatic memories or phobias. Additionally, wearable tech that monitors physiological responses in real-time is enhancing the way therapists and clients understand the body's signals, offering immediate feedback that can guide therapeutic interventions. These innovations are not only broadening the scope of somatic therapy but also making it more accessible and tailored to individual needs.

The Role of Community

The power of community in the healing process cannot be overstated, and somatic therapy is increasingly recognizing and leveraging this force. Group-based somatic practices are gaining traction, providing spaces where individuals can explore their bodily experiences within a supportive community setting. These groups offer the dual benefits of personal exploration and collective healing, creating a shared energy that amplifies the therapeutic impact. Moreover, the rise of online platforms has fostered global communities where practitioners and clients can connect, share experiences, and learn from each other.

This collective engagement is enriching the practice with a diversity of perspectives and experiences.

Looking Ahead

As we peer into the future of somatic therapy, several trajectories suggest exciting developments and challenges. On one hand, the integration of somatic practices into mainstream healthcare offers the potential for wider recognition and application, promising to bring these transformative techniques to a broader audience. On the other hand, this growth necessitates rigorous training and certification processes to ensure the fidelity and quality of somatic practices as they become more widely adopted. Moreover, the ongoing exploration of somatic therapy's applications, from enhancing athletic performance to supporting aging populations, hints at the vast potential of this modality to contribute to various aspects of human well-being.

THE FIELD of somatic therapy stands on the cusp of significant evolution, buoyed by emerging research, innovative practices, and the strengthening role of community. These developments are exciting as they promise to deepen our understanding of the body-mind connection, as well as expand the reach and efficacy of somatic healing. As we move forward, the insights gained from these innovations will undoubtedly reshape the essence of therapeutic practices, offering new pathways to well-being that honor the profound wisdom of our bodies.

NINE

JOURNALING AS A SOMATIC COMPANION

If you could hold a mirror to your soul, one that reflects not just thoughts and visages but the very vibrations of your being, what would it show?

Well, dear reader, your journal is your mirror. It listens, absorbs, and speaks back in whispers of insight and bursts of revelation. Journaling in the context of somatic therapy and shadow healing is a dialogue with the deepest parts of yourself, a practice as simple as it is profound, mystically turning the intangible into something concrete.

In a world where we're constantly bombarded with stimuli, journaling offers a pause, a moment to breathe and connect deeply with ourselves. It's akin to sitting down with an old friend in a cozy cafe, where the hustle of the world fades into the background, leaving space for honest conversations. Here, in the quiet, we find clarity.

Enhancing Self-Awareness

Journaling acts like a personal archaeologist, gently excavating the layers of our experiences to reveal the artifacts of our inner world. It encourages a heightened awareness of the body's whispers and screams, often ignored in the rush of daily life. By documenting physical sensations, we begin to notice patterns and triggers that were previously shrouded in the subconscious. For example, after a long day, sitting down to write about a persistent tension in your shoulders might reveal its connection to an overlooked emotional stressor, offering a chance for recognition and release.

Processing Emotions

Writing provides a safe haven for emotions, a place where they can be expressed without judgment or immediate consequences. It allows for the distillation of feelings, transforming nebulous emotions into clear, manageable entities.

Strengthening the Mind-Body Connection

In somatic therapy, the interplay between mind and body is central. Journaling about bodily experiences brings this connection to the forefront, creating a tangible record of the body's language. This practice honors your body's role in your emotional life and strengthens your relationship with it.

Supporting Memory and Reflection

Journaling serves as a chronicle of our healing process, each entry a snapshot in time. This archive becomes a resource for reflection, allowing us to track our progress, celebrate victories, and learn from challenges. On days filled with doubt, looking back at earlier entries can provide tangible proof of how far you've come, reigniting hope and determination.

Embarking on a somatic healing journey through journaling can be a transformative process. This section provides a comprehensive guide to help you tune into your body's sensations and emotions, and capture them effectively in your journal. By using the provided flowchart, templates, and tips, you'll create a personal space to explore and enhance your somatic awareness.

Tips for Creating a Conducive Journaling Atmosphere

Setting: Choose a quiet, comfortable spot with minimal distractions. You might prefer a nature setting, a designated corner of your home, or anywhere that feels safe and calming.

Mood: Enhance the atmosphere with elements that help you relax and focus. This might include soft lighting, soothing music, or a few drops of lavender oil.

Timing: While you can journal at any time, many find early morning or late evening to be ideal for reflective practice. Choose a time when you are least likely to be interrupted.

Materials: Use a journal that feels personal and inviting. Whether it's a simple notebook or a beautifully bound journal, choose one that inspires you to write. Keep a favorite pen handy—one that flows easily across the page.

Routine: Try to establish a regular journaling routine. Consistency helps deepen your somatic awareness and enriches your healing journey.

By integrating these tools and tips into your practice, you'll enhance your capacity for self-awareness and nurture your path towards healing. Remember that each entry and reflection is a step forward, helping to map out the intricacies of your mind-body connection.

———

Flowchart for Tuning into Bodily Sensations and Emotions

1. **Settle Into a Comfortable Space:** Begin by finding a quiet and comfortable place where you won't be disturbed. Sit or lie down in a relaxed posture.

2. **Close Your Eyes and Breathe:** Take a few deep breaths to center yourself. Focus on the rhythm of your breathing and allow your mind to quiet.

3. **Scan Your Body:** Slowly scan your body from head to toe. Notice any areas of tension, discomfort, or ease without trying to change anything.

4. **Acknowledge Emotions:** As you scan, pay attention to any emotions that arise. Are they linked to specific physical sensations or memories?

5. **Deepen Your Focus:** Choose one physical sensation or emotion to focus on more deeply. Observe its qualities—is it sharp, dull, moving, or constant?

6. **Reflect on Context:** Think about any events or circumstances that might be influencing these sensations and emotions.

7. **Prepare to Journal:** Open your eyes and prepare your journaling materials. Keep your focus

on the sensation or emotion as you transition to writing.

8. **Journal:** Write freely about what you observed. Don't worry about grammar or style; let your experiences flow onto the page.

9. **Reflect and Relax:** After journaling, spend a few minutes reflecting on the experience. Close the session with a few deep breaths, acknowledging your work and healing.

Tip: To break the ice, try writing a letter to your body, thanking it for its resilience and expressing your intentions to listen more attentively to its needs.

My Somatic Journal

This section is dedicated to providing you with thought-provoking journaling prompts that will help you explore the deep connections between your body and emotions. These are designed to encourage you to tap into bodily sensations and emotions, observing and developing a profound understanding of the interplay between the two. Use these prompts as starting points to ignite introspection and discovery in your writing sessions.

Guided Journal Prompts for Emotional Release

In the quiet moments of reflection, journaling bridges the unspoken truths of our bodies with the stories we tell ourselves.

Journaling, in the context of somatic therapy, is an important practice of turning inward, of listening deeply, and of speaking truths. It also happens to be a bridge between the seen and the unseen, the conscious and the subconscious, the body and the mind. Regularly engaging with these prompts can dramatically increase your somatic awareness and emotional understanding. By reflecting deeply through journaling and exploring the answers that come forth, you build a richer connection to your internal world.

This section presents a series of prompts designed to facilitate a deeper conversation with oneself, a dialogue with our being, touching on sensations, emotions, healing, and gratitude. These questions are your allies, guiding you to explore your inner world with an open mind.

Prompts for Exploring Bodily Sensations

- On waking, take a moment to scan your body from head to toe. What are the first sensations that greet you? Describe them without judgment, as if you're a curious observer discovering a new landscape.
- Consider a recent moment of stress or discomfort. Can you recall where in your body you felt it the most? Write about that sensation as if it were a character in a story. What does it want to say?
- Reflect on a time when you felt completely at ease. What physical sensations accompanied this state? Describe these feelings with as much detail as possible, noting any changes in your breath, muscle tension, or posture.

Prompts for Identifying and Processing Emotions

- Think of an emotion that's been prominent for you lately. Where do you feel it in your body? Describe this emotion's texture, weight, and temperature as if you're explaining it to someone from another planet.

- Recall an encounter or event that triggered a strong emotional response. Write about the experience focusing on the physical sensations that arose with the emotion. How did your body react in the moment, and what did it communicate to you?
- Imagine your emotions as weather patterns in the landscape of your body. What kind of weather have you been experiencing lately? Write a weather report detailing the emotional climate, including any storms, calm periods, or unexpected changes.

Prompts for Envisioning Healing

- Visualize yourself in a state of complete healing and balance. What does this version of you look, feel, and act like? Describe your day from start to finish, focusing on the sensations and emotions that accompany this healed state.
- Write a letter to yourself from a future where you have healed from your current challenges. What words of wisdom or encouragement does your future self-have for you? What steps did they take to achieve this state of well-being?
- Reflect on a fear or barrier that feels like it's hindering your healing process. Now, imagine overcoming it. Write about this victory, focusing on how your body feels before, during, and after this breakthrough.

Prompts for Gratitude and Positive Experiences

- Start your day by listing three bodily sensations you're grateful for. These could be as simple as the warmth of your bed or the feeling of your feet on the ground. How do these sensations contribute to your sense of well-being?
- Think of a time when your body surprised you with its strength, resilience, or intuition. Write a thank-you note to your body for that moment, acknowledging its role in your life.
- Reflect on the positive experiences that your body has made possible for you. Choose one memory and dive deep into the sensations associated with it. What role did touch, taste, sight, smell, or hearing play in this positive experience?

In using these prompts, the aim is to uncover the layers of experience that reside within, to listen deeply to the whispers and shouts of your body and emotions, and to document this journey with honesty and openness.

Remember, there is no right or wrong way to respond to these prompts—the goal is to explore and discover what is true for you in your somatic journey. As you hold your pen and face the blank page, remember that this is not just about filling lines but about opening a dialogue with yourself, one that holds the potential to reveal, heal, and transform.

Body-Mind Dialogues: Writing as Conversation

In the quiet spaces where thoughts meander and emotions oscillate, there exists a potent form of communication waiting to be tapped into: the dialogue between body and mind. This conversation, often drowned out by the raucousness of daily life, holds keys to unlocking inner conflicts and maintaining a harmonious relationship between our physical and mental selves. Through the practice of writing dialogues, we can create a bridge for these two aspects of our being to converse, negotiate, and integrate.

Introducing Dialogues

If you've previously explored the practices of shadow work and inner child healing, you have most likely already tapped into the framework of this exploratory activity.

Imagine sitting at a table where both your body and mind are invited to speak, each granted the freedom to express their truths without interruption. This is the essence of body-mind dialogues. It's a method that transcends simple reflection, moving into the realm of active engagement with the various facets of our self. Here, the body might voice its exhaustion or tension, while the mind might articulate worries or dreams. The act of writing becomes the medium through which this conversation unfolds, offering new insights into our inner workings.

Guidance for Conducting Dialogues

To embark on this journey of dialogue, consider the following steps, designed to ensure authenticity and openness.

1. Set the Stage: Find a quiet spot where you feel at ease. Have your journal and pen ready, creating a space that feels inviting for this intimate conversation.
2. Invite Both Parties: Mentally extend an invitation to both your body and mind to participate in this

dialogue. Acknowledge their presence and express your intention for open communication.

3. Begin the Conversation: Start with a greeting or a question. For example, you might write, "Body, how are you feeling today?" Allow the response to flow naturally onto the page, without censorship.

4. Alternate Voices: Switch between speaking as your body and as your mind. This might feel odd at first, but soon you'll find a rhythm to the exchange. Remember, this isn't about grammatical perfection but about genuine expression.

5. Explore Deeper: Don't shy away from tough topics. Use this dialogue to probe into areas of tension, discomfort, or curiosity. Ask your body why it holds stress in certain areas or inquire about the emotions lurking beneath physical sensations.

Examples of Dialogues

To illustrate, here are snippets from hypothetical dialogues that reveal the potential depth of these conversations.

Body: "My shoulders are tight with the weight of carrying burdens not mine to bear." Mind: "I recognize this. It's time we set boundaries to protect our peace."

Mind: "I'm swirling in a storm of anxiety about the future." Body: "Let's find our anchor in the breath, grounding ourselves in the now."

The goal here is to allow the mind to speak freely, without the habitual conscious "ego" chatter. With practice, the answers you seek will seem to appear instantaneously, as though spoken by your higher self or in the form of intuitive messages. This is often the result of subconscious communication. These dialogues are powerful and can illuminate the interconnectedness of physical sensations and mental states, guiding us toward understanding and action.

Reflecting on Dialogues

After engaging in a dialogue, reflection is key. This isn't about analyzing each word but rather sitting with the emotions and revelations the conversation has stirred. Consider:

- Noticing Shifts: Has the dialogue brought a sense of relief, clarity, or further questions? Sometimes, simply giving voice to our body and mind can shift our inner landscape.
- Identifying Patterns: Look for recurring themes or concerns. These patterns can signal areas in need of attention or healing.
- Planning Action: If insights call for change, sketch out gentle steps forward. Perhaps the body requests more rest, or the mind seeks creative outlets for anxiety.
- Gratitude: Finally, extend gratitude to yourself for engaging in this dialogue. Acknowledge the courage it takes to listen and the wisdom found in the conversation.

The act of keeping a written record of these dialogues is another powerful tool for self-discovery. As we continue to engage in these conversations, we cultivate a relationship with ourselves that is rooted in compassion, understanding, and unity.

On the path to healing, journaling emerges as a faithful partner. It holds the space for every nuance of progress, from the subtle shifts in bodily awareness to the profound leaps in emotional healing. This section invites you to explore journaling as a ritual of tracking and celebrating your growth, a way to map the terrain you've navigated and to illuminate the path ahead.

Journaling as a Tracking Tool

Here are a few tips to harness journaling as a tool for tracking mental, emotional and physical changes:

1. Daily Check-ins: Make it a habit to jot down how you feel each day, noting any bodily sensations or emotions that arise. Pay attention to the rhythm of your breath, the tension in your muscles, or the flutter of excitement in your belly. These daily notes become breadcrumbs, leading you through the forest of your healing process.

2. Emotional Landscapes: Whenever you find yourself riding the waves of intense emotions, turn to your journal. Document these moments with as much detail as possible, describing what triggered the emotion, how it felt in your body, and how you navigated through it.

3. Bodily Maps: Occasionally, draw a silhouette of your body in your journal and mark areas where you frequently experience sensations, be it tension, warmth, or tingling. Over time, these maps reveal patterns, showing you where emotions

tend to lodge in your body and how they shift as you heal.

Identifying Patterns and Milestones

As your journal fills with entries, it will begin to reflect some patterns of your healing journey. Here's how to spot them:

• Recurring Themes: Look for emotions or sensations that appear frequently in your journal. Do certain situations or thoughts consistently trigger a knot in your stomach or a tightness in your chest? Recognizing these themes can help you identify the core issues that need attention.

- Healing Milestones: Celebrate moments when you notice a shift in your patterns. Perhaps you handled a situation that would have previously sent you into a tailspin with grace and calm. Such milestones are beacons of progress, illuminating how far you've come.
- Triggers and Responses: By tracking your triggers and how you respond to them, you can gain insights into your coping mechanisms. Over time, you'll notice shifts in your reactions, marking significant progress in your healing journey.

Reflective Questions for Journaling

To deepen your engagement with the healing process, pepper your journaling practice with reflective questions. These inquiries invite introspection, challenging you to look beyond the surface and shedding some light on your experiences. Here are a few questions to get you started:

- What sensation in my body caught my attention today, and what might it be telling me?
- When did I feel most connected to myself this week, and what was happening at that moment?
- How has my response to a familiar trigger changed over time, and what does that say about my healing process?
- In what ways have I shown kindness and patience to myself today?

Celebrating Growth

Throughout all these practices, it is vital to pause and honor your growth. These moments of celebration, whether for monumental breakthroughs or the quiet victories, are the heartbeat of your journey. They will remind you that every step forward, no matter how small, is a triumph.

Gratitude Entries: Dedicate journal entries to acknowledge and express gratitude for your progress. This could be as simple as thanking yourself for taking the time to sit and breathe or for the courage to face a difficult emotion head-on.

Victory Jar: Alongside your journal, keep a victory jar. Each time you recognize a moment of growth, write it down on a piece of paper and add it to the jar. Watching it fill up over time is a powerful visual reminder of your journey.

Letters to Future Self: Write letters to your future self, celebrating the milestones you've achieved. These letters, filled with hope and pride, become time capsules of your resilience, ready to be revisited in moments of doubt.

Within the scope of self-discovery and healing, the act of journaling evolves into an art form when infused with creative expression. This fusion of drawing and writing opens new doors to understanding your inner world, making the intangible, tangible. Colors, shapes, and textures can intertwine with words to narrate the stories of your body and mind in a language that's uniquely yours.

Incorporating Drawing into Journaling

Drawing, sketching, or doodling in your journal serves as a powerful conduit for emotions and sensations that words can't fully capture. This visual vocabulary adds depth to your somatic explorations, offering a different dimension to your reflections. Here are ways to include this practice into your journaling:

- Start with a symbol or shape that resonates with your current physical or emotional state. It doesn't require artistic skill; it's about capturing the essence of your feelings.
- Use colors to express emotions. Warm colors might represent energy or agitation, while cool colors could signify calm or detachment. Notice how color choice reflects your inner landscape.
- Sketch the sensations in your body. A tight knot in your stomach, the flutter of anxiety in your chest, or the warmth of happiness might translate into specific images or abstract forms on the page.

These visual elements are important as they reflect a

dialogue with yourself, revealing layers of your experience that might remain hidden under the surface of words alone.

Expressive Writing Techniques

Moving beyond traditional journaling, expressive or intuitive writing taps into the subconscious, allowing for a raw and unfiltered exploration of thoughts and feelings. Techniques such as stream of consciousness and poetic forms enrich this practice.

Stream of consciousness writing bypasses the analytical mind, letting thoughts and emotions flow onto the page without censorship or judgment. One way to do it involves setting a timer and writing non-stop, capturing whatever comes to mind.

You may also feel drawn to experiment with poetic forms to distill emotions and experiences into concentrated expressions. Haikus, free verse, or rhymed couplets can all convey the intensity or subtlety of your feelings in unique ways.

Combining Words and Visuals

The synergy between words and visuals in your journal creates even more valuable insight into your inner space. This combination allows for a multi-layered exploration of the somatic journey, where each element enhances the other.

You can choose to annotate your drawings with words, adding context or insights that the images evoke. This could be a single word, a question, or a longer reflection. Moreover, surrounding your written entries with doodles or sketches that emerge as you write can highlight emotions or themes in your text, providing another layer of understanding. Creating pages that alternate between written entries and visual expressions is also a good idea, allowing you to notice how each mode of expression influences the other.

Encouraging Experimentation

The journey through somatic therapy is deeply personal, and the way we express and integrate this experience is equally individual. I encourage you to experiment in your journaling practice to invite a sense of play and discovery.

Try different mediums such as watercolors, ink, or collage to express various states or shifts in your somatic experience. Each medium can evoke different emotions and insights.

Rotate your journaling practice through different settings — outdoors, in a quiet room, or in a café. Notice how the change in environment influences your creative expression.

Share your journaling journey with a trusted friend or therapist. Discussing your drawings and writings can offer new perspectives and deepen your understanding of your somatic experience.

CREATIVE JOURNALING IS a central aspect of navigating the complexities of our somatic journeys. In this practice, we find a space to honor our experiences, to see them laid out in color and form, in words that dance across the page.

TEN

TOOLS FOR TRANSFORMATION

As you step into the world of somatic therapy, you will continue to discover a variety of techniques and exercises that await, ready to cater to your personal healing needs. Your willingness to explore and experiment is the only prerequisite.

Now, let's roll up our sleeves and dive into the first tool in your kit: grounding technique cards.

Grounding Technique Cards: A DIY Toolkit

When our world feels like it's spinning too quickly, finding moments of stillness and connection can seem like a rare treasure. Grounding techniques pull us back from the tumult of our thoughts and emotions to the solid earth beneath our feet. Imagine creating a personalized toolkit, one that fits neatly in the palm of your hand, ready to offer support and steadiness whenever needed. This section guides you on crafting your own set of grounding technique cards, turning abstract concepts into tangible allies in your quest for balance and calm.

Creating Grounding Cards

The process of making these cards is as therapeutic as their use. Begin with gathering your materials - cardstock or thick paper, colored pens or markers, and any other decorations that speak to you. Each card will represent a different grounding technique, a visual and textual reminder of the tools at your disposal. Here are a few steps to get you started:

1. Decide on the Size: A deck that's easy to carry allows for spontaneous use. Consider sizing your cards to fit in a standard card holder or a small pouch.
2. Outline Your Techniques: Before you start decorating, list the grounding techniques you want to include in your deck. Aim for a variety that addresses both physical and emotional needs.
3. Design Your Cards: On one side of the card, write the name of the grounding technique. On the other, describe the practice briefly and add any visual cues or symbols that resonate with the method. This could be as simple as a calming color for a breathing exercise or a drawing of roots for a visualization technique.

Suggestions for Grounding Techniques

Your deck should reflect practices that you find personally effective. Here are some techniques you may want to include, each with its unique way of bringing you back to the present:

- Five Senses Exercise: A method that involves naming something you can see, touch, hear, smell, and taste, engaging all your senses to ground you in the now.

- Focused Breathing: Breathing deeply and slowly, with attention on the breath's path in and out of your body, can serve as a powerful anchor.
- Nature Connection: Techniques that encourage a tactile connection with the natural world, like holding a stone or visualizing roots growing from your feet into the earth.
- Muscle Relaxation: Progressive muscle relaxation, where you tense and then slowly release different muscle groups, can release physical tension and mental stress.

Using the Cards

With your deck at the ready, incorporate these cards into your daily routine or turn to them in moments of distress. They can be used in various ways:

- Daily Draw: Start or end your day by drawing a card at random, using the chosen technique as a focus for grounding.
- Situation-Specific Selection: In moments of anxiety or overwhelm, sift through your deck and choose a technique that feels most suited to your current needs.
- Shared Practice: Use the cards as a way to introduce grounding techniques to friends or family members, encouraging collective moments of calm and connection.

Personalization and Creativity

The beauty of this toolkit lies in its capacity for personalization. As you become more familiar with grounding practices, you might discover new techniques that resonate with you. Update your deck to reflect these discoveries, keeping it dynamic and aligned with your evolving needs.

Here are some ideas to infuse your cards with creativity and personal significance:

- Artistic Flair: Use colors, drawings, or symbols that hold personal meaning or simply bring you joy. The process of decorating your cards can itself be a meditative and grounding practice.
- Inspirational Quotes: If certain words or quotes inspire calm and presence for you, consider including these on your cards as additional support.
- Texture and Sensation: Incorporating textures, such as fabric swatches or embossed patterns, can add a tactile element to the cards, enhancing the grounding experience.

The creation and use of grounding technique cards embody the principle that small acts, performed with intention, can have profound impacts on our well-being. They also remind us that we already possess the tools necessary to anchor ourselves, to find moments of peace amidst the chaos. As you craft, personalize, and utilize your deck, let each card be a stepping stone back to yourself, a tangible reminder of your capacity for calm and resilience.

In the realm of healing through somatic therapy, we know that movement holds a key role, acting as both a mirror and a map. It reflects our inner states, translating emotions and traumas into physical expressions, and guides us toward understanding and integration. The Movement Exploration Log serves as a companion in this process, offering a structured way to document your engagement with various forms of movement. This methodical approach aids in recognizing the impact of movement on your journey through trauma, enabling you to tailor your practices to your unique path toward healing.

Guidance for Movement Documentation

The log is designed to be user-friendly, encouraging regular entries without feeling like an added burden. Here's how it's structured:

- Type of Movement: Whether it's yoga, dance, walking, or another form, specify the activity. This helps in identifying which practices resonate most with you.
- Duration: Note how long you engaged in the movement. This isn't about aiming for a certain time but observing how different durations affect you.
- Emotional and Physical Responses: After each session, record any emotions that surfaced, along with physical sensations. Was there a sense of relief, joy, or perhaps discomfort? How did your body feel during and after the movement?

- Contextual Factors: Were there external factors that influenced your experience? Perhaps the time of day, your environment, or your energy level played a role.

This systematic approach helps track what you do, whilst painting a picture of how movement supports your healing.

Prompts for Reflection

To deepen your engagement with the log, reflection prompts guide you beyond mere observation, encouraging a dialogue with yourself about the nuances of each experience. Some prompts include:

- How did this movement practice shift your energy or mood?
- Did any specific memories or insights arise during or after the movement?
- How does engaging in this type of movement align with your current needs or healing goals?
- Can you identify any resistance or hesitation toward certain movements? What might this indicate?

These questions are not meant to elicit right or wrong answers but to foster a deeper understanding of your relationship with movement and its role in your healing journey.

Patterns and Preferences

Over time, the log becomes a rich source of data, revealing patterns and preferences that can inform your healing process.

You may discover that certain movements consistently evoke joy and energy, while others might bring up discomfort or resistance. Recognizing these patterns is invaluable, as it guides you to practices that nourish and support you while also challenging you to confront and work through more difficult emotions or memories.

To identify these patterns, look for:

- Repetitive emotional or physical responses to specific types of movement.
- Times of day or contexts in which movement feels most beneficial.
- Any correlation between the duration of movement and its impact on your mood or energy levels.

This awareness allows you to make informed choices about which practices to incorporate more regularly into your routine and which ones to approach with caution or additional support.

Encouraging Variety

While identifying what works best for you is essential, there's also immense value in variety. Different movements can stimulate the body and mind in unique ways, offering a broader spectrum of healing opportunities.

Try experimenting with new forms of movement that you haven't tried before. If you typically engage in slow, meditative practices like yoga, try something more dynamic, like dance or martial arts.

Changing your environment is another way to embrace variety. If possible, practice movement both indoors and outdoors, noting how the change in setting influences your experience.

You could also choose to attend classes or workshops. This can introduce you to new types of movement and offer the added benefit of community support.

Whichever you choose, the goal here is to expand your expressive range, exploring various avenues of movement to uncover what facilitates the deepest healing.

Maintaining Your Somatics Routine

Creating a rhythm in life that includes somatic self-care practices can sometimes feel like trying to maintain a delicate balance. The somatic self-care checklist provides a stable center from which to balance our daily and weekly commitments with the nurturing practices our bodies and minds need.

Comprehensive Self-Care Checklist

To ensure a holistic approach, this checklist encompasses a range of practices from body scanning and grounding to movement and breathwork. It's designed to be a living document, one that evolves along with you, adaptable to your changing needs and circumstances.

My Self-Care Checklist

Morning Rituals:

1. Grounding Technique:

- Start your day by connecting with the present moment and grounding yourself. This could involve:
- Standing barefoot on the ground and feeling the support of the earth beneath you.
- Visualizing roots extending from your feet into the ground, anchoring you in stability and strength.
- Practicing grounding affirmations or mantras to affirm your presence and resilience.

2. Mindful Breathing:

- Begin your day with a few minutes of mindful breathing to cultivate inner calm and centeredness:
- Practice deep breathing exercises, such as the 4-7-8 technique or box breathing, to regulate your nervous system and reduce stress.
- Use a mindfulness app or guided meditation to guide your breathing practice and bring focus to the present moment.

Midday Moments:

1. Short Mindful Movements:

- Incorporate brief moments of mindful movement throughout your day to rejuvenate your body and mind:
- Take short breaks to stretch your body and release tension, focusing on areas of tightness or discomfort.

- Practice simple yoga poses or qigong exercises to promote flexibility and energy flow.
- Perform a quick body scan to check in with your physical sensations and address any areas of discomfort or imbalance.

2. Mindful Awareness Breaks:

- Integrate mindful awareness breaks into your daily routine to pause and reconnect with yourself amidst busy tasks:
- Take a few deep breaths and observe your surroundings without judgment, using your senses to anchor yourself in the present moment.
- Practice mindful eating by savoring each bite of your meals, paying attention to flavors, textures, and sensations.
- Engage in a brief mindfulness practice, such as a 3-minute breathing space or body scan, to reset your focus and calm your mind.

Evening Wind-Down:

1. Longer Session of Movement Practice:

- Wind down your day with a longer session of movement practice to release accumulated tension and promote relaxation:
- Engage in a gentle yoga flow or restorative yoga sequence to soothe your body and quiet your mind.

- Incorporate self-massage techniques, such as foam rolling or trigger point therapy, to release muscular tension and promote relaxation.
- Go for a leisurely walk in nature to unwind.
- Dance freely to your favorite music, allowing movement to be a form of self-expression and emotional release.

2. Dedicated Breathwork Exercise:

- End your day with a dedicated breathwork exercise to release stress and prepare for restful sleep.
- Practice abdominal breathing to activate the body's relaxation response and promote deep relaxation.
- Experiment with alternate nostril breathing to balance the left and right hemispheres of the brain and calm the nervous system.
- Use a guided breathwork meditation specifically designed for relaxation and inner peace.

Other Holistic Self-Care Practices:

1. Shadow Work:

- Dedicate time for shadow work, the process of exploring and integrating the unconscious aspects of the self:
- Journaling prompts: Reflect on your fears, insecurities, and unresolved emotions to bring them into conscious awareness and explore their underlying roots.

- Creative expression: Use art, writing, or other forms of creative expression to explore and express aspects of yourself that may have been suppressed or ignored.
- Inner dialogue: Engage in compassionate self-talk and inner dialogue to nurture acceptance and integration of all parts of yourself, including the shadow aspects.

2. Nature Connection:

- Connect with nature as a source of healing and rejuvenation:
- Spend time outdoors, whether it's a walk in the park, gardening, or simply sitting under a tree.
- Practice grounding exercises in nature, such as walking barefoot on the grass or lying down and feeling the support of the earth beneath you.
- Cultivate a sense of awe and gratitude for the natural world, observing the beauty and interconnectedness of all living beings.

3. Community and Support:

- Prioritize building and nurturing supportive relationships with others:
- Reach out to friends, family members, or support groups for emotional support and connection.
- Participate in group activities or classes that align with your interests and values, fostering a sense of belonging and community.

- Seek professional support from therapists, counselors, or coaches who can provide guidance and assistance on your self-care journey.
- Remember, it's important to listen to your body and intuition to determine which practices resonate most with you at any given time. Allow this checklist to evolve and adapt as you grow and change, continually exploring new avenues to support your overall well-being.

Customization Tips

To make this checklist truly yours, consider these personalization strategies:

- Adjust the timing and duration of practices based on your schedule and energy levels. Some days might allow for a longer morning ritual, while others might require shorter, more focused exercises.
- Experiment with different techniques to discover what resonates most with you. This might mean trying various grounding methods or exploring new movement activities.
- Listen to your body and mind. They will guide you toward what practices are most needed at any given time. This intuitive approach ensures your self-care routine remains relevant and nurturing.

Reflection and Adjustment

Treating this checklist as a flexible guide rather than a rigid schedule allows for growth and adaptation. Reflection is key to this process. Weekly check-ins with yourself to assess what's working and what needs tweaking can be incredibly enlightening. Questions to consider might include:

- Which practices have become non-negotiable parts of your day or week?
- Have you noticed any shifts in your physical or emotional well-being since integrating certain practices?
- Are there techniques that no longer serve you or that you're curious to explore further?

Adjustments based on these reflections ensure your somatic self-care routine remains aligned with your evolving needs, providing a solid foundation from which to navigate life's fluctuations. With time and consistency, the act of maintaining this routine will become a meaningful ritual, a way to honor the connection between your body and mind, and to nurture the balance that sustains you.

As WE WRAP up this chapter, remember, the aim here is not to add more to your plate but to integrate practices that bring you back to a state of balance and harmony. Make room for moments that reconnect you with yourself, ensuring that amidst the busyness of life, you remain grounded, aware, and present.

ELEVEN

THE POWER OF COMMUNITY IN SOMATIC HEALING

As human beings, we are deeply wired for connection. When we embark on a personal healing journey, opening up to others and creating connections can seem quite challenging. However, it is also a crucial time to push past this discomfort and forge meaningful connections.

Creating your own community by surrounding yourself with individuals drawn together by a commitment to self-awareness and personal development can be life changing. This becomes a space where shared experiences and collective wisdom light up the path to personal growth and recovery.

In our fast-paced world, where individual achievement often takes center stage, the power of community in the healing process can sometimes be overlooked. Yet, there's something profoundly transformative about coming together with others who understand the nuances of somatic experiences. A place of refuge, learning, and connection.

Shared Experiences Foster Healing

When someone else articulates what you've felt but haven't found the words for, it's like a light being turned on in a dark room. Suddenly, you see that you're not alone in your struggles. Group settings, whether in person or online, provide a platform for these moments of connection. They remind us that our personal battles are part of a larger narrative, one that connects the lives of many. In sharing our stories, we unburden ourselves and light the way for others.

Consider the simple act of breathing together in a guided somatic workshop. There's a rhythm, a collective pulse that synchronizes individual energies. This act, seemingly basic, can profoundly influence our sense of belonging and shared humanity. It reinforces the idea that healing isn't just an individual endeavor; it's a communal voyage.

Community as a Resource

Learning from others who've navigated similar paths can offer invaluable insights and shortcuts to our own healing. Community acts as a living library, rich with resources, strategies, and support systems. From practical advice on integrating somatic practices into daily routines to recommendations for professional help, the collective knowledge within a community is a goldmine waiting to be tapped.

For instance, within a community meeting where members share their favorite grounding techniques, one person may mention how walking barefoot on grass helps them feel present, while another talks about the calming effect of mindful baking. Each suggestion adds to a collective repository of strategies, offering new tools for managing stress and anxiety.

Likewise, a discussion group focused on polyvagal theory can uncover a multitude of ways to engage the vagus nerve for relaxation—from singing and humming to cold water face immersion. Hearing how others apply these concepts in real life can spark creativity in our healing practices, encouraging us to experiment and find what resonates with our unique needs.

There's so much wisdom in numbers. When individuals from diverse backgrounds come together, they bring unique perspectives and experiences that enrich the collective understanding of healing. This mosaic of insights can challenge our assumptions, open our minds to new possibilities, and inspire innovative approaches to somatic therapy.

Overcoming Isolation

One of the greatest challenges on the healing path is the feeling of isolation that often accompanies deep personal work. Finding a community breaks through this isolation, offering a sense of companionship and mutual support. It's comforting to know there are others who not only understand what you're going through but are also rooting for your success.

Support groups, whether focused on specific techniques like TRE (Trauma Release Exercises) or broader topics like trauma recovery, can significantly reduce feelings of loneliness. They provide a safe space to express vulnerabilities, celebrate progress, and offer encouragement during setbacks.

Community Connection Exercise

Welcome to the Community Connection Exercise, an interactive activity designed to help you reflect on your current support system, identify any gaps, and set intentions for enhancing your community connections. Grab a pen and some paper, and let's get started.

Step 1: Listing Existing Support

TAKE a few moments to jot down the names of people and groups who currently provide support in your life. This could include:

- Friends
- Family members
- Therapists or counselors
- Support groups (e.g., recovery groups, hobby clubs)
- Online communities

Write down as many as you can think of, no matter how big or small their role may seem.

_____

_____

_____

_____

_____

_____

_____

_____

_____

_____

_____

_____

Step 2: Identifying Gaps

Now, consider areas where you feel there might be a lack of support or connection in your life. Reflect on aspects like:

- Emotional support
- Practical assistance (e.g., help with tasks or responsibilities)
- Intellectual stimulation
- Spiritual guidance
- Social interaction

Write down any areas where you feel you could benefit from additional support or connection.

_____

_____

_____

_____

_____

_____

_____

_____

_____

_____

_____

Step 3: Setting Intentions

BASED ON YOUR REFLECTIONS, set some actionable intentions for enhancing your community connections. Consider steps like:

- Reaching out to someone new for support or companionship
- Joining a local club or group related to your interests or hobbies
- Seeking out a mentor or counselor who aligns with your goals and values
- Volunteering in your community to connect with others and contribute to a cause you believe in

Write down at least one intention that feels achievable and meaningful to you. Feel free to brainstorm additional ideas as well.

_____

_____

_____

_____

_____

_____

_____

_____

_____

_____

_____

_____

Take a moment to review what you've written and to acknowledge the support that already exists in your life. Try to recognize any areas where you'd like to cultivate more connections. Remember, building community is an ongoing process, and it's okay to start small. By taking intentional steps to enhance your community connections, you're investing in your own well-being and creating a stronger support network for yourself.

Feel free to revisit this exercise whenever you feel the need to reassess your community connections and set new intentions for growth. Your support system is a valuable resource on your healing journey.

Online Forums and Groups: Connecting Virtually

In a world where digital landscapes stretch far and wide, online forums and groups present a unique opportunity. Spanning across geographical divides, they bring together individuals passionate about somatic therapy from all corners of the globe. The virtual world holds space for experiences, thoughts, and support, available at the click of a button.

Accessing Global Support

Imagine tapping into a wellspring of collective knowledge and empathy that spans continents. Online forums and groups dedicated to somatic therapy provide this exact opportunity. Here, you can find others who share your interests, challenges, and aspirations. Whether you're seeking advice, looking to share your own journey, or simply wanting to feel understood, these virtual communities can be a rich resource. They offer a sense of belonging that transcends physical boundaries, creating a global support network that's accessible anytime, from anywhere.

Finding the Right Fit

With the vast array of online communities available, finding one that resonates with your specific needs and values is crucial. Here are some tips to guide your search:

- Research: Start by exploring various platforms known for hosting supportive communities, such as Reddit, Facebook, or specialized forums. Look for groups that focus on somatic therapy, trauma recovery, or holistic healing.
- Read the Room: Spend some time lurking in potential groups. Observe the interactions, the types of posts, and the overall tone. Does it feel welcoming? Is there a sense of mutual respect and understanding?
- Privacy Matters: Consider the privacy policies of the forum or group. Some might be open, while others may require approval to join. Decide what level of privacy you're comfortable with, especially when it comes to sharing personal experiences.
- Trial and Error: Don't hesitate to join a few groups to get a feel for them. You can always leave if they don't meet your expectations. Finding your virtual tribe might take some time, but it's worth the effort.

Engaging Safely

While online forums and groups offer invaluable support,

navigating them safely is paramount. Here are guidelines to ensure your virtual interactions remain positive and secure:

- Protect Your Information: Be mindful of the personal details you share. Use discretion when discussing sensitive aspects of your healing journey, and consider the potential implications of sharing identifiable information.
- Respect Boundaries: Just as in face-to-face interactions, respecting others' boundaries online is essential. Engage with empathy and kindness, and avoid offering unsolicited advice.
- Digital Etiquette: Remember the human behind the screen. The anonymity of the internet can sometimes lead to misunderstandings. Strive for clear communication and assume positive intent whenever possible.
- Seek Credible Sources: When exchanging resources or advice, prioritize information from reputable sources. This ensures the guidance you receive and offer is based on sound principles and practices.

Maximizing Virtual Connections

To transform your online interactions into meaningful connections, consider these strategies:

- Active Participation: Contribute to discussions, ask questions, and share insights. Active engagement helps build rapport with other members, making the experience more fulfilling.

- Virtual Meetups: Some groups organize virtual meetups or workshops. Participating in these events can deepen your connection with the community and provide opportunities for real-time interaction.
- Peer Support: Look for opportunities to offer or receive one-on-one support. Many forums have mechanisms for connecting members seeking individualized advice or companionship on their healing journey.
- Celebrate Milestones: Share your progress and celebrate the achievements of others. Recognizing growth and milestones fosters a positive environment and encourages continued engagement.

In the digital age, the quest for connection and understanding in the realm of somatic healing need not be a solitary one. Online forums and groups offer a platform for collective wisdom, empathy, and support that can significantly enrich your healing process. By approaching these virtual communities with mindfulness, respect, and a willingness to engage, you open the door to a world of connections.

Local Somatic Therapy Groups: Finding Your Tribe

The warmth of real-life connections, the energy of shared physical space, and the tangible support from local communities hold a unique charm in the healing process. When you step into a room with others who are on similar paths, the air fills with an unspoken understanding and empathy that digital platforms can struggle to replicate. This section sheds light on the significance of local somatic therapy groups, offering insights into discovering these communities and making the most of the invaluable support they provide.

The Advantages of Local Groups

Local somatic therapy groups offer a sanctuary where healing practices are discussed and experienced collectively. The live interaction and immediate feedback elevate the learning process, allowing for a deeper immersion in somatic practices. Here, the nuanced guidance from facilitators and the spontaneous sharing of insights add layers to your understanding that solo practice or virtual groups might miss. Being physically present with others also fosters a stronger bond, making every session an opportunity to build lasting support networks that extend beyond therapy sessions.

Resources for Finding Local Somatic Therapy Groups

Discovering a local group that feels right can be like finding a hidden gem. It requires some searching, but the rewards are well worth the effort. Start with:

- Community Centers and Wellness Clinics: Often, these local hubs host or can connect you to ongoing somatic therapy groups. They might also offer workshops or introductory sessions to give you a taste of different practices.
- Online Directories and Websites: Many professional somatic therapists and facilitators advertise their groups on dedicated websites or through therapy directories. A quick search can reveal options in your vicinity, complete with

reviews and ratings to help you make an informed choice.

- Social Media and Local Forums: Local community boards on platforms like Facebook or Nextdoor can be surprisingly resourceful. Members often share information on upcoming group sessions or can direct you to known facilitators in the area.

Tips for Active Participation

Once you've found a group that resonates with you, diving in with an open heart can significantly amplify your experience. Consider:

- Volunteering: Offer to help with organizing sessions or events. It's a great way to deepen your engagement with the group and show your commitment.
- Sharing Your Journey: When comfortable, share your experiences and insights. Your story could be the encouragement or breakthrough moment for someone else.
- Practicing Regularly: Consistency strengthens your connection to the group and enhances the benefits of somatic practices. Try to attend sessions regularly, making them a priority in your schedule.

Local somatic therapy groups offer a unique blend of personal growth, shared healing, and community building. By actively participating in these groups, you can tap into a collective strength. Whether through community centers, online platforms, or social media, finding your tribe is a step towards not just individual healing but also towards contributing to a larger ecosystem of support and understanding. Make your journey less solitary and more interconnected.

Creating Your Own Support Group

Laying the Foundation: Setting Intentions

So, you've decided to take the lead and start your group. Now what?

Before you call the first meeting or send out an invitation, take a moment to reflect on the group's purpose. What do you hope to achieve? Is it to explore specific somatic practices, offer support for personal healing, or share knowledge and experiences? Writing down these intentions can guide the group's direction and ensure that activities align with these foundational goals.

- Define the group's focus: Be clear whether the group will concentrate on general somatic therapy practices or if it will cater to specific interests or needs, such as stress reduction or trauma recovery.
- Establish core values: What principles will your group embody? Consider inclusivity, confidentiality, respect, and mutual support as potential cornerstones.
- Set realistic expectations: Understand that the group will evolve over time. Flexibility and openness to change can help manage expectations for yourself and future members.

Finding Members and Creating a Safe Space

With your intentions set, the next step is to invite others to join your garden of growth. Finding members who share your interest in somatic therapy can begin within your existing networks or by reaching out to broader communities.

- Reach out to your network: Start with friends, family, or acquaintances who have expressed interest in somatic therapy or personal growth. Personal invitations can make individuals feel valued and welcomed.
- Utilize social media and community boards: Post in relevant online forums, community boards, or social media groups. Be clear about the group's intentions and whom it's for.
- Choose a conducive meeting space: Whether it's a quiet room in a community center, a private home, or a tranquil outdoor space, ensure the environment feels safe, welcoming, and suitable for group activities.

A crucial aspect of creating a conducive environment is establishing ground rules that prioritize safety and confidentiality. These rules should be discussed and agreed upon by all members from the outset.

Facilitating Group Dynamics

Dynamics within a support group require much care and attention. Facilitating a group where every member feels heard, valued, and connected involves several key practices:

- Foster open communication: Encourage members to share their thoughts, feelings, and experiences. Active listening and empathy should be promoted as fundamental group behaviors.

- Manage conflicts with care: Disagreements or misunderstandings may arise. Address these openly and constructively, aiming to strengthen the group rather than divide it.
- Celebrate diversity: Acknowledge and embrace the varied backgrounds, experiences, and perspectives within the group. This diversity can enrich the learning and healing process for everyone.

Organizing Group Activities

Activities are the heart of the support group, providing shared experiences that can deepen connections and facilitate healing. When planning activities, consider the group's intentions and the interests of its members.

Shared practices: Regularly include somatic exercises, such as guided body scans, mindful movement, or breathing techniques that members can experience together.

Guest speakers: Invite somatic therapists, experienced practitioners, or experts in related fields to share their knowledge and insights with the group.

Group discussions: Allocate time for members to discuss topics related to somatic therapy, personal growth, or healing. These discussions can foster a sense of community and collective wisdom.

Sustaining the Group Over Time

For a support group to thrive, it requires ongoing care and attention. Here are strategies to ensure its longevity and vitality:

- Leadership rotation: Consider rotating the facilitator role among members. This can distribute responsibility, offer varied perspectives, and keep the group dynamic fresh.
- Member engagement: Regularly check in with members about their needs, interests, and suggestions for the group. This feedback can guide adjustments and improvements.
- Scheduled check-ins: Establish periodic meetings to reflect on the group's progress, revisit intentions, and make any necessary changes to its direction or structure.

CREATING your own somatic therapy support group is an opportunity to bring individuals together in pursuit of healing, growth, and connection. By setting clear intentions, fostering a supportive environment, and nurturing the group's development, you can cultivate a space where members feel empowered to explore somatic practices and share their journeys.

CONCLUSION

As we prepare to close this chapter—not just of the book but of our initial foray together into the transformative world of somatic therapy—I find myself reflecting on the beauty and complexity of this journey. Somatic therapy, with its profound capacity to heal and integrate the mind, body, and spirit, reflects the deeply personal yet universally relevant path toward holistic healing. It is a journey as unique as each leaf on a tree, yet as connected as the forest they form.

Throughout these pages, we've navigated the core principles of somatic therapy, emphasizing the importance of body awareness, the grounding influence of mindfulness, the liberating power of movement, the nurturing practice of developing a somatic self-care routine, and the unparalleled support found within a community.

The key takeaways, I hope, are as vivid in your mind as they are in mine: the inextricable link between mind, body, and spirit; the profound wisdom our bodies hold; and the empowerment that blossoms from engaging with somatic practices.

Together, we've unveiled the transformative potential of somatic therapy to not only release trauma and alleviate anxiety but to guide us toward a profound sense of inner peace.

I urge you, dear reader, to continue this exploration beyond the confines of this book. The journey to healing and self-discovery is not a destination but a continuous path, enriched with new practices, insights, and the ever-present potential for growth and change. Dive deeper, experiment with courage, and embrace the evolution of your healing practice with an open heart.

Remember, the significance of community and support in our healing journey cannot be overstated. Whether through virtual connections, local gatherings, or the shared space of professional therapy, finding your tribe offers a wellspring of understanding and encouragement. Healing, in many ways, is a shared journey, illuminated by the collective wisdom and compassion of those we walk with.

And so, I call upon you to take charge of your healing journey. Let the tools, insights, and practices shared in these pages guide you toward empowerment. Somatic therapy is not merely a method for healing; it is a call to live more fully, more authentically, embracing the full spectrum of human experience.

I acknowledge that this path is not without its challenges. There will be moments of doubt, of regression, of feeling lost in the wilderness of our own healing. Yet, it is in these moments that our resilience shines brightest. Your courage to embark on this journey, to face the shadows and seek the light, is a testament to the strength of the human spirit.

Thank you for your trust, your openness, and your willingness to explore the realms of somatic therapy. I am most grateful for your companionship on this journey. Remember, you are never alone. There is a world of support, understanding, and love waiting to embrace you.

As we part ways, I invite you to view somatic therapy not just as a series of practices but as a holistic approach to life. Integrate its principles into your daily existence to form a continuous, sacred connection between your mind, body, and soul. Let this book be a starting point, a springboard into a life lived with depth, awareness, and an unshakeable connection to the essence of who you are.

MAY your journey be filled with discovery, healing, and an abundance of peace.

POSTSCRIPT

I'd love to hear your thoughts...!

 As an independent author with a small marketing budget, **reviews** are my livelihood on this platform. If you enjoyed this book, I would truly appreciate it if you left your honest feedback.

YOU CAN DO this by clicking the link to *The Somatic Therapy Handbook* on www.amazon.com.

. . .

ADDITIONALLY, you can jump in and join our well-being community via https://www.facebook.com/groups/theemerald society, or contact me directly at ydgardens@emeraldsocpublishing.com.

I PERSONALLY READ every single review, and it truly warms my heart to hear from my readers.

WITH KINDNESS,
  Yas

BONUS 1: SOMATIC HEALING JOURNAL PROMPTS

Exploring Physical Anchors of Emotion

Choose an emotion you've felt recently. Where in your body do you feel this emotion most intensely? Describe the physical sensations associated with this emotion in as much detail as possible.

_____

_____

_____

_____

_____

_____

_____

_____

_____

_____

_____

Mapping Emotional Triggers

Think about a recent situation that triggered a strong emotional response. What physical reactions accompanied these emotions? How did your body posture or sensations change with your feelings?

_____

_____

_____

_____

_____

_____

_____

_____

_____

_____

_____

_____

The Dialogue Between Body and Mind

Reflect on a day this past week. Write a conversation between your body and your mind about how they experienced the day differently. What might each say about the other's response to stress or joy?

_____

_____

_____

_____

_____

_____

_____

_____

_____

_____

_____

Revisiting a Past Experience

Think of a significant event from your past and focus on remembering how your body felt during this event. What do those sensations tell you about your emotional state at that time?

Sensory Walk

Take a short walk and focus solely on your bodily sensations
with each step. After your walk, journal about the experience.
What did you notice that you normally overlook?

_____

_____

_____

_____

_____

_____

_____

_____

_____

_____

_____

_____

Breath as a Pathway

Sit quietly and focus on your breathing for a few minutes. How does the rhythm of your breath change with different thoughts or emotions? Write about the connection you observe between your breathing patterns and your current state of mind.

_____

_____

_____

_____

_____

_____

_____

_____

_____

_____

_____

_____

Physical Manifestations of Joy and Pain

Identify one moment of joy and one of pain from your life. Describe how each was manifested physically in your body. How did your environment, thoughts, or actions influence these sensations?

_____

_____

_____

_____

_____

_____

_____

_____

_____

_____

_____

The Story of a Scar

If you have a physical scar, write about the incident that caused it, focusing on the bodily sensations before, during, and after the event. How does this physical scar connect to your emotional ones?

_____

_____

_____

_____

_____

_____

_____

_____

_____

_____

_____

_____

_____

Chronic Tensions and Their Tales

Consider any chronic tension or pain in your body. What emotions might be linked to these persistent sensations? Explore possible events or unresolved feelings contributing to this state.

Healing Through Movement

Engage in a gentle form of movement that you enjoy (e.g., yoga, stretching, dancing). Reflect on how your emotional and physical states shift with movement. What does this tell you about your body's needs and your emotional wellbeing?

_____

_____

_____

_____

_____

_____

_____

_____

_____

_____

_____

_____

_____

BONUS 2: BODY SCAN REFLECTION TEMPLATE

Date/Time: _____

Current Mood: _____

Physical Manifestation of Emotion:

- Head: _____
- Shoulders: _____
- Chest: _____
- Arms: _____
- Stomach: _____
- Legs: _____

Emotional State: _____

Associated Thoughts/Memories:

_____

Overall Reflection:

_____
_____
_____
_____
_____
_____
_____
_____
_____
_____
_____
_____

THE EMERALD
S O C I E T Y

JOIN OUR TRIBE

The Somatic Therapy Handbook

*A Transformative Guide to Trauma Recovery, Anxiety Relief,
Nervous System Regulation and Releasing Emotional Blockages
by Connecting Mind, Body & Soul*

REFERENCES

- *Breathing: the legacy of Wilhelm Reich* https://www.sciencedirect.com/science/article/pii/S1360859299800291

- *How Does Somatic Experiencing Therapy Work?* https://www.verywellmind.com/what-is-somatic-experiencing-5204186

- *Post-traumatic stress disorder: the neurobiological impact* ... https://www.ncbi.nlm.nih.gov/pmc/articles/PMC3182008/

- *What is CBT vs. Somatic Therapy? - North Carolina* ... https://www.nccenterforresiliency.com/somatic-articles/what-is-cbt-vs-somatic-therapy/

- *Post-traumatic stress disorder: the neurobiological impact* ... https://www.ncbi.nlm.nih.gov/pmc/articles/PMC3182008/

- *Body Awareness: How to Deepen Your Connection with* ... https://www.healthline.com/health/mind-body/body-awareness

- *Breathing to reduce stress - Better Health Channel* https://www.betterhealth.vic.gov.au/health/healthyliving/breathing-to-reduce-stress

- *5 Incredible Stories of Self-healing and Transformation* https://somaticmovementcenter.com/healing/

- *Body Scan Meditation: Benefits and How to Do It* https://www.verywellmind.com/body-scan-meditation-why-and-how-3144782

- *Buddhist Antecedents to the Body Scan Meditation* https://www.buddhismuskunde.uni-hamburg.de/pdf/5-personen/analayo/buddhistantecedentsbodyscan.pdf

- *Bodysensing: Learn to Listen to Your Body in Meditation* https://www.yogajournal.com/meditation/meditation-classes/bodysensing-learn-listen-body-meditation/

- *Evoking calm: Practicing mindfulness in daily life helps* https://www.health.harvard.edu/blog/evoking-calm-practicing-mindfulness-in-daily-life-helps-202110142617

- *Effects of Mindfulness on Psychological Health: A Review ...* https://www.ncbi.nlm.nih.gov/pmc/articles/PMC3679190/

- *30 Grounding Techniques to Quiet Distressing Thoughts* https://www.healthline.com/health/grounding-techniques

- *Effect of breathwork on stress and mental health - Nature* https://www.nature.com/articles/s41598-022-27247-y

- *How nature benefits mental health* https://www.mind.org.uk/information-support/tips-for-everyday-living/nature-and-mental-health/how-nature-benefits-mental-health/

- *Impact of dance therapy on adults with psychological trauma* https://www.ncbi.nlm.nih.gov/pmc/articles/PMC10334851/

- *Yoga For Emotional Release: 8 Postures For Peace* https://www.brettlarkin.com/yoga-for-emotional-release/

- *Effectiveness of Dance Movement Therapy in the ...* https://www.frontiersin.org/articles/10.3389/fpsyg.2019.00936/full

- *5 Ways to Make Your Home a Healing Space* https://www.psychologytoday.com/us/blog/how-healing-works/202005/5-ways-make-your-home-healing-space

- *The Benefits of Somatic Movement* https://totalsomatics.com/the-benefits-of-somatic-movement/#:~:text=Somatic%20movement%20helps%20to%20alleviate,system%2C%20breathing%20and%20heart%20rate.

- *Trauma Recovery: Stages and 7 Things to Consider* https://www.healthline.com/health/mental-health/trauma-recovery

- *Integrating Somatic Learning into Everyday Life* https://www.jstor.org/stable/1585773

- *Somatic Awareness Journaling: A simple daily practice to* ... https://kristyarbon.com/somatic-awareness-journaling/

- *7 deep breathing exercises to help you calm anxiety* https://www.calm.com/blog/breathing-exercises-for-anxiety#:~:text=The%204%2D7%2D8%20breathing%20technique%20is%20a%20method%20that,a%20state%20of%20deep%20relaxation.

- *Mindfulness-Based Interventions for Anxiety and Depression* https://www.ncbi.nlm.nih.gov/pmc/articles/PMC5679245/

- *Real Stories of SE* https://traumahealing.org/real-stories-of-se/

- *The Importance of the Outdoor Environment for the Recovery* ... https://www.ncbi.nlm.nih.gov/pmc/articles/PMC9915437/#:~:text=(1)%20Background%3A%20Research%20has,as%20part%20of%20their%20treatment.

- *Somatic Experiencing Therapy: 10 Best Exercises & ...* https://positivepsychology.com/somatic-experiencing/

- *Polyvagal Theory Explained (& 18 Exercises & Resources)* https://positivepsychology.com/polyvagal-theory/

- *On The Importance of Titration for Trauma Healing (10 Benefits)* https://www.new-synapse.com/aps/wordpress/?p=1842

- *Somatic Mindfulness: What Is My Body Tellin...- GoodTherapy* https://www.goodtherapy.org/blog/somatic-mindfulness-what-is-my-body-telling-me-and-should-i-listen-0619185/#:

- *Efficacy of journaling in the management of mental illness:* https://www.ncbi.nlm.nih.gov/pmc/articles/PMC8935176/

- *Mind/Body Awareness Writing Exercises* https://www.fammed.wisc.edu/files/webfm-uploads/documents/outreach/im/handout_mbs_workbook.pdf

- *100+ Self-Care Journal Prompts for Healing and Reflection* https://blog.gratefulness.me/self-care-journal-prompts/

- *Writing Therapy: How to Write and Journal Therapeutically* https://positivepsychology.com/writing-therapy/

- *Body Scan Meditation: Benefits and How to Do It* https://www.verywellmind.com/body-scan-meditation-why-and-how-3144782

- *30 Grounding Techniques to Quiet Distressing Thoughts* https://www.healthline.com/health/grounding-techniques

- *Body- and Movement-Oriented Interventions for ...* https://www.ncbi.nlm.nih.gov/pmc/articles/PMC6973294/

- *Breathwork for Healing Trauma: 3 Popular Techniques ...* https://www.othership.us/resources/breathwork-for-healing-trauma

- *The Role of Community Support in Mental Health Recovery:* https://www.fundamentalchange.life/the-role-of-community-support-in-mental-health-recovery

- *What Is Online Group Therapy? Plus, How to Find it* https://www.healthline.com/health/mental-health/online-group-therapy

- *Guide to Starting a Support Group* https://iocdf.org/ocd-finding-help/supportgroups/how-to-start-a-support-group/

- *How To Set Social Media Boundaries To Protect Your Mental Health:* https://mindfulhealthsolutions.com/how-to-set-social-media-boundaries-to-protect-your-mental-health/

- *Somatic Therapy: Benefits, Types And Efficacy – Forbes Health* https://www.forbes.com/health/mind/somatic-therapy/#:

- *10 Somatic Interventions Explained* https://integrativepsych.co/new-blog/somatic-therapy-explained-methods

- *Somatic experiencing – effectiveness and key factors of a ...* https://www.ncbi.nlm.nih.gov/pmc/articles/PMC8276649/

Integrating Somatic Practices into Everyday Life — Repose https://byrepose.com/journal/integrating-somatic-practices-into-everyday-life

Manufactured by Amazon.ca
Acheson, AB

13602062R00134